EASY
CROSSWORDS
ON-THE-GO!

Martin Ashwood-Smith,
Harvey Estes, and Frank Longo

Main Street
A division of Sterling Publishing Co., Inc.
New York

2 4 6 8 10 9 7 5 3 1

Published by Sterling Publishing Co., Inc.
387 Park Avenue South, New York, NY 10016
© 2006 by Sterling Publishing Co., Inc.

The material in this book has been excerpted from
the following Sterling Publishing Co., Inc. titles:
Sip & Solve Easy Crosswords © 2005 by Frank Longo
10-Minute Crosswords © 2005 by Martin Ashwood-Smith
Crosswords for a Rainy Day © 2006 by Harvey Estes

Distributed in Canada by Sterling Publishing
C/o Canadian Manda Group, 165 Dufferin Street
Toronto, Ontario, Canada M6K 3H6
Distributed in the United Kingdom by GMC Distribution Services
Castle Place, 166 High Street, Lewes, East Sussex, England BN7 1XU
Distributed in Australia by Capricorn Link (Australia) Pty. Ltd.
P.O. Box 704, Windsor, NSW 2756, Australia

Sterling ISBN-13: 978-1-4027-4408-2
ISBN-10: 1-4027-4408-0

For information about custom editions, special sales, premium and
corporate purchases, please contact Sterling Special Sales
Department at 800-805-5489 or specialsales@sterlingpub.com.

CONTENTS

Short and Sweet Crosswords

1

ACROSS

1 More than chubby
6 Jordanian or Kuwaiti, e.g.
10 Very eager
12 "If I Had a Hammer" singer
13 *Lord of the Rings* fiend
14 Old Spanish coin
15 Friendly
17 Cotton bundle
18 Reach via phone
20 *Symphonie Espagnole* composer Edouard
22 Sculpts
24 Homer, to Bart and Lisa
25 Acknowledged, as one's error
27 Computerists' phrase often rendered as "P2P"
28 *So Big* novelist Ferber
29 Hospital divisions

DOWN

1 *What the Butler Saw* playwright Joe
2 Purposely obstructed, as a street
3 "All By Myself" singer
4 Transgression
5 Geraint's patient wife
6 Discordant-sounding
7 Its rungs may be made of hemp
8 Based on how old one is
9 Old TV clown
11 Eloquent but unconvincing
16 TV's "Mistress of the Dark"
19 Riga resident
21 Stenches
22 Batman's cover-up
23 Pack away
26 Litter-loathing org.

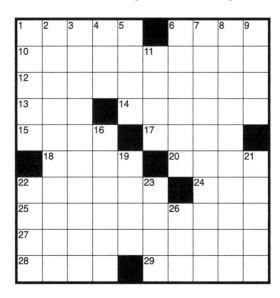

2

ACROSS

1 Not liquid or gaseous
6 Toward shelter, at sea
10 Novelist Jong
11 Having no value
12 Building demolisher, e.g.
13 World's longest river
14 Witchcraft
16 Studier of Middle Eastern culture
17 Correction smudge
20 Comment about a bit of personal misfortune
24 Actor Jannings
25 Big name in tinfoil
26 The "C" of UPC
27 Nice ___ (prude)
28 Very, in Versailles
29 "Peachy-keen!"

DOWN

1 Belgrade resident
2 Spoken
3 Ms. Minnelli
4 1979 film about a blinded figure skater
5 Jamaican alcohol
6 Title girl of a Poe poem
7 Mario's brother, in Nintendo games
8 Immigrants' island
9 Vote in
15 Gilligan's Island girl
17 Tape deck button
18 Grapevine story
19 Parenthetical remark
21 Bruins' sch.
22 Young horse
23 Send to the canvas, in boxing lingo

3

ACROSS

1 Coffin carrier
11 Warship covering
12 Item on a drop-down computer list, e.g.
13 1987 Pet Shop Boys hit
14 #1 hit
17 ___ de France
18 Bare-bones bed
19 Ditties
21 From Yemen or Oman
24 Philatelists' treasures

28 Excessive, insincere bits of praise
29 Estrogen or testosterone

DOWN

1 *Mork & Mindy* costar Dawber
2 Exist
3 K-O linkup
4 Jazz trumpeter Armstrong
5 Soup liquid
6 *The Mod Squad* costar Omar
7 Utah ski resort
8 Shriveled-up grape
9 Prima ballerina

10 City in northwest France
14 Neck warmers
15 Team spirit
16 Prescription antihistamine brand
19 ___-Tots (Ore-Ida product)
20 Take weapons away from
22 One of Louisa May Alcott's "Little Women"
23 "That's all there ___ it!"
25 "O Sole ___"
26 Ballpoint, e.g.
27 Opposite of NNW

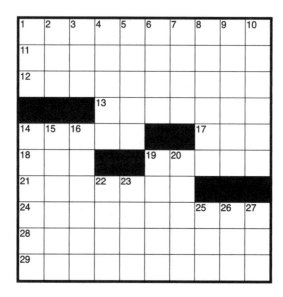

8

4

ACROSS
1 Moe or Curly
7 Twisty letter
10 Actress Bullock
11 Little louse
12 Eats away at
13 "It's freezing in here!"
14 Novell systems-management package
16 Virginia locale also known as Fair Oaks
19 States of being
20 Criminal's photo ID
21 Ugandan tyrant Amin
22 Golfer Omar
26 ___ Aviv
27 Primping aid
28 Koch and McMahon
29 Sink bowls

DOWN
1 Dallas-to-Houston dir.
2 Pothole fill
3 Lennon's love
4 Peculiarity
5 Gift for gardening
6 Central Illinois city with a riverboat gambling casino
7 With full judiciary authority
8 "Yes ___, Bob!"
9 Place emphasis on
15 Snowy seasons
16 Jew
17 Oozed out
18 Night watches
23 ___ Lanka
24 2,000 pounds
25 Taxing org.

5

ACROSS

1 2000 Best Actor winner Russell
6 Jazz singer Anita
10 Like porridge or granola
11 Heap
12 Getting older
13 Braggarts have big ones
14 Craftsman's cutter
16 Sets straight
17 Made a metallic ringing sound
20 Complete influence
24 *I Shot Andy Warhol* costar Taylor
25 Dietary roughage
26 Opposed to, in backwoods slang
27 Wear away
28 Fork prong
29 Actress Zellweger

DOWN

1 Use gentle persuasion on
2 Hindu melody
3 Of the ear
4 Connected to the Internet
5 Feed frenziedly
6 Began shooting
7 "Let's eat!"
8 In the air
9 Positive responses
15 Large, brownish-red pear
17 B's equivalent, musically
18 Playwright Pirandello
19 Dog-tired
21 Black, to bards
22 Surrender formally
23 Squirrel's hangout

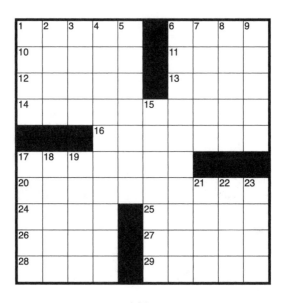

ACROSS
1 "Famous" cookie man
5 *R.U.R.* playwright Capek
10 Folks who hit the jackpot
12 Not legally allowed to drive
13 Squirrels away
14 "Electric" swimmers
15 Dweebs
19 Rough version
21 Now's partner
22 Dirty, dilapidated dwelling
24 Awareness of right and wrong
27 First thing taken by a waiter, usually
28 Lip-___ (mouths the words)
29 Antis' votes

DOWN
1 Ill-treated
2 Worker making money?
3 Teton Indian
4 Monetary unit in Bern
5 Attacked with one's leg
6 She played the mother in *My Mother the Car*
7 Hi-___ monitor
8 Before, to bards
9 Trip-inducing drug
11 "___ bin ein Berliner"
16 Girl in a Beach Boys title
17 *Frasier* star Grammer
18 Smiles like a villain
20 Speeches
23 "General" on a Chinese restaurant menu
24 *ER* roles
25 Suffix with access or direct
26 ___ Tin Tin (TV dog)

7

ACROSS

1 "Gimme All Your Lovin'" band
6 Syrup sources
10 Weighing a lot
11 Give off
12 UFO's whereabouts
14 Mouse click, e.g.
15 Do intentionally
16 Meshes well with the group
20 Place for King Arthur and his knights
25 Correctly placed
26 Truth twister
27 Alternative to Canon or Ricoh
28 Tennis shoe securer
29 *Thelma & Louise* costar Davis

DOWN

1 Communist leader ___ Enlai
2 Supreme Greek god
3 London art gallery
4 In charge of
5 Egyptian wonders
6 Nasal partitions
7 At full speed, old-style
8 Ornamental embroidery loop
9 Office worker using shorthand
13 Filling with an aroma
16 Ruffle
17 Ancient Greek region
18 Rapper ___ Shakur
19 Nap noisily
21 End in ___ (require overtime)
22 Ten-speed, e.g.
23 Ducklike diving bird
24 Sicilian summer resort

8

ACROSS

1 Make it to the next grade
5 One imitating a dove
10 Director Preminger
11 Request to a blackjack dealer
12 Say whatever comes to mind
14 Author
15 Pass one through another
20 City near downtown Detroit
21 Triangular sail
22 Hints from Heloise, e.g.
26 Enter, as computer data
27 *The Sopranos* actress Falco
28 Mag about Internet business
29 McNally's mapmaking partner

DOWN

1 Baked entrée with a pastry crust
2 Wise Greek goddess
3 Is frugal to a fault
4 Shakespearean poem
5 Barbecue briquette composition
6 Lubricate
7 Siouan Indian
8 Ostrichlike bird
9 Ruby or scarlet
13 With a sudden muffled thud
16 John of *Three's Company*
17 Lake or city in central New York
18 Break up a fight, e.g.
19 Felt in one's bones
22 Guitar at a luau
23 Construct
24 Pupil's place
25 Cry of disgust

9

ACROSS
1 The same
6 "Woe is me!"
10 Rosalind Russell title role
12 Ontario newspaper
13 Candor
14 German city in which Einstein was born
16 Be like-minded
17 Civil rights org.
20 NFL six-pointers
21 Indirect allusion
24 Bandleader known as "the mambo king"
27 Stuff in a farm trough
28 City or river in Maine
29 Harps' ancient cousins

DOWN
1 Break bread
2 Status ___
3 Not exactly a Casanova
4 At the apex of
5 Conga formation
6 In the company of
7 Contents of some copier cartridges
8 Tickled pink
9 Hearing, touch, and taste
11 Active Sicilian volcano
14 Hall-of-Fame quarterback Johnny
15 Pacific Ocean weather system with a more famous brother
18 Former New York governor Mario
19 Rap's Salt-N-___
22 Void's partner
23 Resist openly
25 Golf ball balancer
26 Magazine VIPs

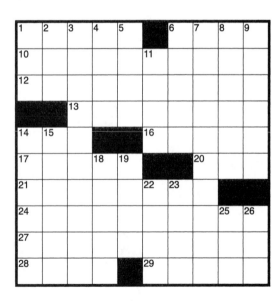

10

ACROSS

1 "Splish Splash" singer
11 "That's my understanding"
12 Of less than standard quality
13 Love letter opening
14 Dined at home
15 Surrenders
16 Dangler on a graduate's cap
20 Actress Verdugo
21 Fact falsifier
25 Cooperative CBer's phrase
27 Coated with varnish
28 Formative time of one's life

DOWN

1 Tie up
2 Clarinet's cousin
3 Second Greek letter
4 Fuzzy image
5 Puppy sound
6 Bit of minutiae
7 Take ___ (decide by show of hands)
8 Fight off
9 "Why? Because ___ so!"
10 Scandinavian fate goddesses
15 Annual
16 Short and to the point
17 Hawaiian hello
18 "Against the Wind" singer Bob
19 Short fishing line
21 Parasites that pester pooches
22 Actress/author Chase
23 Computer brand
24 Curtain supporters
26 Method

1	2	3	4	5	6	7	8	9	10
11									
12									
13				■	14				
■			15						
16	17	18	19			■	■	■	■
20				■	21	22	23	24	
25			26						
27									
28									

11

ACROSS
1 Bit of hearsay
6 Agree (with)
10 Make amends
11 Guesses at JFK
12 Removed the rind from
13 Poet Whitman
14 Mine passage
15 Otherwise
16 1997 Jim Carrey comedy
18 Heyday of Benny Goodman and Artie Shaw
20 Mist
21 Wonder Woman portrayer Carter
24 Eager

25 ___ *Irish Rose* (old Broadway comedy)
26 Diva Horne
27 Andean shrubs whose leaves are chewed
28 On pins and needles
29 Put forth, as power

DOWN
1 Emulates Eminem
2 The Beehive State
3 Being preachy
4 1963 hit for the Chiffons

5 Label on discount merchandise
6 Holder of earrings, necklaces, etc.
7 Snow cone alternative
8 Model airplane wood
9 Fruity-smelling compound
17 Tighten, as skates
18 Oil-bearing rock
19 Gestured "hello"
22 Precious
23 Helper: Abbr.

12

ACROSS
1 Jotter's tablet
11 Merchant ship's path
12 Ella Fitzgerald or Billie Holiday, e.g.
13 Prefix with cycle or sex
14 "For shame!"
15 Cub Scout units
17 Out-of-date
21 Razors' sharp parts
23 Abound (with)
24 Major conflict
26 Pat gently
27 "I Heard a Rumour" band
31 Pro at public relations

32 Voracious predator of warm seas

DOWN
1 Children's Research Hospital in Memphis
2 Stretched, as the neck
3 Tearing down
4 Wood-shaping tool
5 Midterm or final
6 Hard but easily breakable
7 Warn from behind the wheel

8 Wrinkly-faced dog
9 Gobbled up
10 ___ *Rosenkavalier* (Strauss opera)
16 Wastewater
18 "Breaking Up Is Hard to Do" singer
19 Tailor, at times
20 Get on board
22 More rational
25 Ewes' mates
27 Drill attachment
28 French friend
29 Pester
30 Pep rally yell

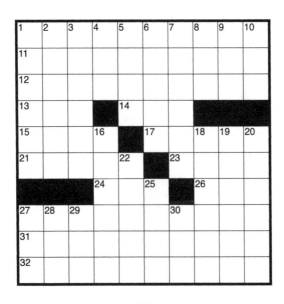

ACROSS

1 Arctic coat
6 Musical symbol before the key signature
10 Washday challenge
11 Fog
12 Inspiring reverence in
13 Gumbo vegetable
14 *Blue Sky* Best Actress winner Jessica
15 Posterior
16 Santa's other half
18 Place for a rake or a hoe
21 Grungy guy
23 *Amo*, translated
24 Copy a contented cat
25 "Yes, ___!" ("You betcha!")
26 ___ mater
27 Long side up
28 Rumple
29 Hatchlings' hangouts

DOWN

1 Sacred song
2 Fighting ferociously
3 Gullywashers
4 They're the largest of venomous snakes
5 San ___, Texas
6 High-kicking queue
7 Some beachfronts
8 Poet Pound
9 Phobia
17 Pulitzer-winning novelist Lurie
19 Occurrence
20 Ownership papers
21 Junk e-mail
22 Doozy

14

ACROSS
1 Declared openly
7 *Ben-Hur* studio
10 Gilbert & Sullivan's genre
12 What a band member may embark on
13 Bullring cheers
14 Swiss city on the Rhine
15 Swimsuit tops
17 Hereditary British title
20 Helps with a heist
21 Baseballer Aparicio
25 Texas river to Galveston Bay
27 In a deviant way
28 Attorney's concern
29 Luanda is its capital

DOWN
1 As well
2 Renaissance stringed instrument
3 Eye amorously
4 Burning question for *Dallas* fans in 1980
5 Abbr. after a list
6 Not too hard to accomplish
7 Edwin of Reagan's cabinet
8 Actress Garson
9 Friable earthy deposits
11 Talking nonsense
16 Michael who played Cochise on *Broken Arrow*
17 ___ metabolic rate
18 Addis ___ (Ethiopian capital)
19 Extend a subscription
22 Second word of the Golden Rule
23 "___ never work!"
24 Tofu bean
26 Has the ability

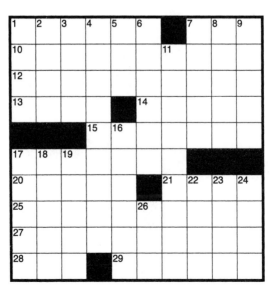

15

ACROSS

1 Windy blast
5 Plumed military cap
10 Object of worship
11 Hit lightly and repeatedly
12 Howard Keel's *Seven Brides for Seven Brothers* costar
14 Occasion for a ribbon-cutting ceremony
15 Big online brokerage
16 Greg's sitcom partner
21 Desktop publisher's concern
25 What many disposable products are designed for
26 *Evita* surname
27 Inquires
28 *Dallas* family name
29 Take it easy

DOWN

1 Bearded, gun-toting doll
2 Go with the flow
3 Solitary sort
4 "Maria ___" (Jimmy Dorsey hit)
5 City near Boston
6 Biker's bike, colloquially
7 Imitated
8 Nut whose extract is used in soft drinks
9 "___ the strong survive"
13 Paltry
17 Once ___ (annually)
18 Shake awake
19 Cologne scents
20 "This is only ___"
21 Catholic bigwig
22 From scratch
23 Former Spice Girl Halliwell
24 Prince William's alma mater

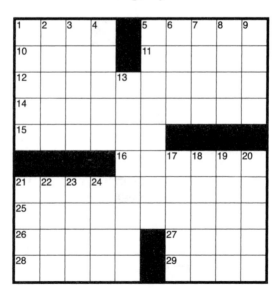

20

16

ACROSS
1 Liquor
6 Pâté de ___ gras
10 Line touting an informercial product
12 National park in Michigan
13 Ocho ___ (Jamaican resort)
14 Chops down
15 Japanese money
16 Fling forcefully
17 Algerian port
19 Cpl.'s superior
22 Spring month
24 Add to the payroll
25 Transferred computer-to-computer, in a way
27 1977 David Lynch cult film
28 Scottish isle for which a terrier breed is named
29 Flavorful

DOWN
1 Hirsute
2 *I'm Not Rappaport* costar Davis
3 Scandinavian capital
4 Mediocre grades
5 That girl
6 Lobby
7 From every direction
8 "___ cost you!"
9 Nights before
11 Not at all enjoyable
16 Best Actress winner Berry
18 Quick wash
20 Terrific
21 Cuddly bedroom bear
22 Fruity drinks
23 Ham or bacon
24 "Very funny"
26 Morsel left at a meal

ACROSS

1 Heavy horn
5 Analyze in a lab
10 #1 hit for the Jackson 5
12 Regards with favor
13 Story
14 Boy Pharaoh
15 Bee sound
17 Sports center
19 Queried
21 Calls a halt to
22 "___ sher!" ("Like, definitely!")
23 In the blink ___ eye
25 More amicable
29 Be inactive, as a volcano
30 Painter Degas
31 ___ gin fizz

DOWN

1 "___ the season ..."
2 New ___, Minnesota
3 Overwhelming all-out attack
4 On fire
5 On a cruise
6 Moo ___ pork
7 Occurring every seven years
8 In the area of
9 Gossipy, meddling women
11 Snaky fish
15 Perplex
16 Logging-on name
18 Domains
20 One giving blood, e.g.
24 Pres. who served four terms
26 Self-help author LeShan
27 Brian of ambient music
28 Numbered highway: Abbr.

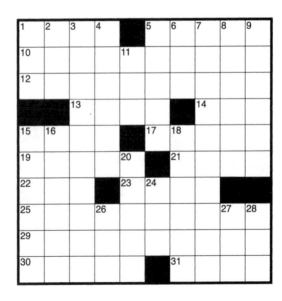

18

ACROSS

1 In many varieties
11 Quite a difficult deed
12 Ali Baba's password
13 Short letter
14 "... ___ a puddy tat!"
15 Burns slightly
17 Stuffing herb
18 Country bumpkin
19 Sat for a portrait
20 WWW address
21 Explorer Vasco da ___

22 Thin, wrinkly giftwrap
26 Crushed by the competition, slangily
27 Water-coast meeting places

DOWN

1 A Beatle bride
2 Vain, appearance-conscious guy
3 Readily accepting
4 Lost maiden in "The Raven"

5 Endures
6 Patella's place
7 Uncertainties
8 Very tidy
9 Do harm to
10 Slow-cooked
15 Las ___, New Mexico
16 Shout of cheer
17 Mogadishu resident
19 Pontifical
21 Chromosome component
23 For each
24 Eden evictee
25 Dwelling place: Abbr.

19

ACROSS

1 Led Zeppelin's "Whole ___ Love"
6 ___ California (Mexican peninsula)
10 Indo-European
11 Frankenstein's humpbacked helper
12 "Much obliged, monsieur!"
13 ___ bladder
14 Library on wheels
16 Cuban cigars
17 Had thoughts
20 1966 Frank Sinatra song
24 Molecule unit
25 Sweetheart
26 Entr'___ (intermission)
27 Actress Massey
28 Star of *Mask* and *Moonstruck*
29 Violinist/actor Zimbalist

DOWN

1 Young flock member
2 Black-and-white cookie
3 Beginner
4 Tool for driving small nails
5 Fill with life
6 Three little pigs' terrorizer
7 One more time
8 La ___ (San Diego resort)
9 French city where van Gogh painted
15 Rest on top of
17 Sci-fi author Asimov
18 From the Netherlands
19 Ham it up onstage
21 Novello of old films
22 State bird of Hawaii
23 Druggist's weight unit

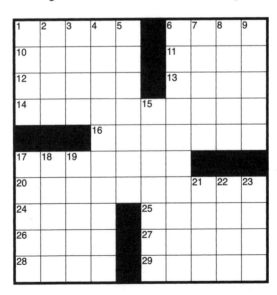

ACROSS

1 Ornamental evergreen of the cypress family
11 Supporter of drapes
12 Carnivores
13 Suffix of superlatives
14 *The Godfather* actor Richard
15 Word before lobe or nudity
17 "Please, I'd rather not hear it!"
20 Emancipated
21 100-lb. unit
24 Capital on the Oregon Trail
27 Guacamole, essentially
28 Statement on a mall directory map

DOWN

1 Highest point
2 Regrets bitterly
3 Spoiled kid
4 Giants giant Mel
5 *Norma ___* (Sally Field film)
6 Global media giant
7 Chant
8 Senator Lott
9 Major artery
10 Ill-fated Ford
15 Coca-Cola brand
16 Sunfish variety
17 Locale of Berkeley and Oakland, briefly
18 City near Salt Lake City
19 Alphabet quintet
21 Suffix with motor or aqua
22 Sound from an electric fan
23 Booze it up
25 Suffix with cyan
26 Homer Simpson's outburst

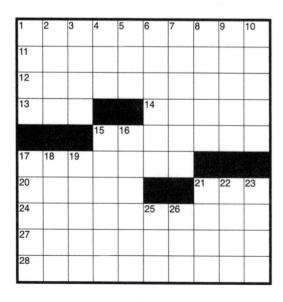

21

ACROSS

1 Dale the chipmunk's chum
5 Oktoberfest dance
10 Misleading clue
12 Took into account
13 *Mr. Belvedere* actress Graff
14 Former competitor of Delta
15 Big ape
18 *Shogun* novelist James
22 Boxer who called himself "the greatest"
25 Locale
26 Two-time *Taxi* Emmy winner
29 "Pet detective" played by Jim Carrey
30 Prepared
31 Prophet

DOWN

1 Jenny of weight loss
2 Phone conversation opener
3 Person doing nothing
4 Pertaining to sound
5 Start for mature or historic
6 Fort ___ (old California military base)
7 Elevate
8 Be familiar with
9 Taj Mahal city
11 *The Seven Year Itch* Tony winner Tom
16 *Alice* title role portrayer Linda
17 Wards off
19 Follow as a result
20 "Filthy" monetary gain
21 *The Merry Widow* composer Franz
22 Slightly open, as a door
23 Writer/politician Clare Boothe ___
24 Notion
27 High-capacity film format
28 The Beatles' "___ Jude"

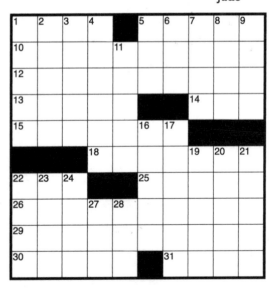

22

ACROSS

1 Scottish Highlands native
5 Self-confident manner
10 Additional
11 Real estate units
12 Experiences again, as one's youth
14 Phrase of empathy
15 ___-wee Herman
16 Lots and lots
17 Old
19 Title of respect in India
20 Amnesia
24 Plainly visible
25 *The Balcony* playwright Jean
26 Rocket-launching org.
27 *"Ad ___ per aspera"* (Kansas's motto)
28 Slender

DOWN

1 Singer Halliwell who was Ginger Spice
2 One of filmdom's Baldwin brothers
3 Harry Houdini's specialty
4 Bent forward at the waist
5 Hors d'oeuvre of puréed liver
6 Microscope's eyepiece, e.g.
7 Lacking in logic
8 Take care of
9 German steel city in the Ruhr valley
13 Opposite of "post-"
17 Alternative to Compaq or Dell
18 Trait carriers
19 Barrett of Pink Floyd
21 Hollywood's Hayworth
22 PC port standard
23 Sewing line

ACROSS

1 Tent-pitching place
5 Shaped like a rainbow
10 Egg on
11 Grinding tooth
12 Overflow points
13 Atlanta university
14 Final
15 ___ Vegas
16 Messy condition
20 "Forever Your Girl" singer
21 Cozy room
22 Lane who sang with Xavier Cugat
23 Aches
25 Lug
26 BP ___ (big name in oil)
27 Romance novelist Victoria
28 Gotten out of bed
29 "The ___ the limit!"

DOWN

1 Get comfy, as a sleeping cat
2 *Jurassic Park* actress Richards
3 Producer of many old musicals
4 Plague
5 Aviator Earhart
6 Ancient soak-and-sweat sites
7 Something beyond comprehension
8 Corn-on-the-cob serving
9 Parched
17 *Cheers* bartender portrayer
18 In a nuanced manner
19 Rains down ice
23 Golf standard
24 "Who ___ to judge?"

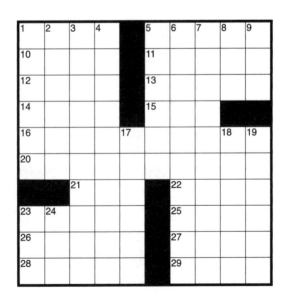

24

ACROSS

1 Entertainment center combo
6 Fish of tropical shore waters
10 *The Evil Dead* director Sam
11 Ring around a saint
12 *Ragtime* novelist
14 Impartial
15 "Gloria in Excelsis ___"
16 City north of Des Moines
17 *The World According to ___*
19 The Chiffons' "___ So Fine"
22 Be noticeably different
25 25-year Nebraska Cornhuskers head coach who became a Congressman
26 Got on in years
27 *Grosse Pointe Blank* costar Alan
28 Schnozz
29 Nodders' answers

DOWN

1 Forced into a difficult situation
2 Heart or trumpet part
3 Penny arcade fixtures
4 "Let's go!"
5 Mary's last name on *The Mary Tyler Moore Show*
6 Glistened
7 Poker-playing predators
8 Plant with soothing juice
9 *Harvey* hero Elwood P. ___
13 Saint Petersburg's inlet
18 Negative battery terminal
20 Bert's roommate
21 British submachine guns
22 Laurel of Laurel and Hardy
23 For takeout
24 Sweat outlet

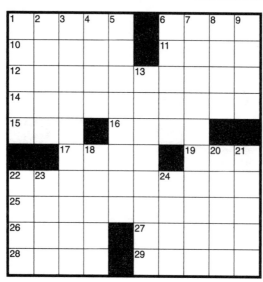

ACROSS

1 Dallas's I-635, familiarly
11 Dublin denizens
12 Altered hereditary unit
13 Ballpark fig.
14 Person in pursuit
15 Bashful
16 Ben-___ (Best Picture of 1959)
17 Abbr. on a battleship
18 Scientist's workplace
21 1972 Lemmon/ Wilder comedy
24 Eggs, biologically
25 Tummy troubles
27 Ocean bottom-dweller with large, winglike pectoral fins
28 Declarations

DOWN

1 Sour fruits
2 Comb alternative
3 Landing pier
4 The Sunshine St.
5 One-story with a low-pitched roof, as a house
6 Ardor
7 ___ Allan Poe
8 Pee-___ Big Adventure
9 "Rule, Britannia" composer Thomas
10 River in France and Belgium
17 Not rented out
18 Mean Girls star Lindsay
19 Turn away in avoidance
20 Soaks up some rays
21 Parisian's "down with"
22 Airhole
23 Bit of green pond growth
26 Fidel cohort Guevara

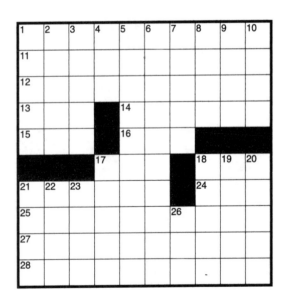

26

ACROSS
1 Whopper alternative, in fast food
7 Ave. crossers
10 Add vitamins to, e.g.
11 Top 40 music genre
12 Half-conscious state
13 "___ changed man!"
14 Brief, sharp fight
15 Fiendish Tolkien creatures
16 Place for a spare bed, often
18 What every criminal suspect is entitled to
19 Supper scraps
20 Trigonometry measurement
22 Words said to be wed
23 Handsome young man
24 Original Beatle Sutcliffe
25 Current
26 Talking-___ (scoldings)
27 Look through casually

DOWN
1 Wagers
2 Apropos of
3 Unwarranted
4 People printing money
5 Confront boldly
6 Revolutionist Guevara
7 Richard Nixon's vice president
8 Drink of gin, soda water, sugar, and lemon juice
9 Involuntary muscle movement
15 Major South American river
17 Brokerage employee
18 Pass off as genuine
21 Punta del ___ (Uruguayan resort)
23 Wall St. wheeler-dealer

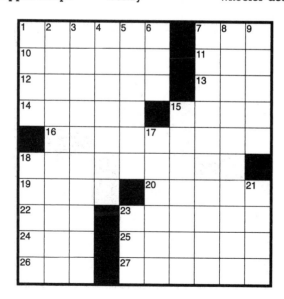

31

27

ACROSS

1 Singing syllable
4 Perps' excuses
10 "That seems probable"
12 Missive available for anyone to read
13 "I'm ___ Wash That Man Right Outa My Hair"
14 First South Korean president Syngman ___
15 Country in the Pyrenees
17 Preadult
21 Kett of old comics
24 "¿Cómo ___?" (Spanish "How are you?")

25 Those adding vitamins to food, e.g.
27 1972 sketch comedy that was Chevy Chase's first film, with *The*
28 Abhorrence
29 Word after chicken or mouse

DOWN

1 River in New York and Pennsylvania
2 Really tease
3 Modify formally
4 Blazing
5 Tell a fib
6 While being shipped

7 Actress Broderick or playwright Henley
8 "It's all clear now"
9 Ticked off
11 One jotting in the margins
16 Shortened a sail
18 Consumed completely
19 Greta who played Mata Hari
20 Newark, New Jersey's county
21 D-I connection
22 1970 war epic, when tripled
23 Jogging pace
26 "___ had it up to here!"

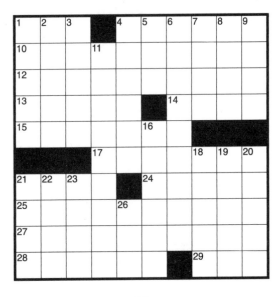

28

ACROSS
1 Female horse
5 Cowboy's cry
10 Wild Eurasian goat
11 Reef surrounding a lagoon
12 Cajole
13 Bundled up hay
14 Folk singer Guthrie
15 Consecrate
16 Letter-printing aids
18 More X-rated
21 Oscar nominee
23 Concerning
24 Thick slices
25 Leonardo da Vinci's ___ Lisa
26 Protruding belly button
27 City in northern Oklahoma
28 Senses by touch
29 Senses by sight

DOWN
1 Flaky minerals
2 End prematurely, as a mission
3 Property in buildings and land
4 World's largest oil company
5 Bugs Bunny, to Elmer Fudd
6 Constantly
7 Rare golf shots
8 Corrida cheers
9 Cutlass Supreme maker
17 Uses four-letter words
19 Golfer Els or Sergeant Bilko
20 Enjoys a novel
21 Starting from the date
22 Sleuth's aid

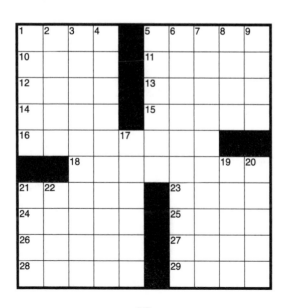

ACROSS
1 Easily duped people
5 Ermine in its brown summer coat
10 Hawaiian dance
11 *Brideshead Revisited* novelist Evelyn
12 Unwritten exam
13 Jazz clarinetist Shaw
14 Private learning institutions without boarding facilities
16 Indian woman's dress
17 Hillary Clinton, ___ Rodham
18 In the style of

20 ___-Romeo (sports car)
22 Areas where a very valuable element is mined
26 Concerning
27 Try to shed a few pounds
28 Tubular pasta
29 Award for a TV show
30 Double-___ sword
31 Microsoft video game system

DOWN
1 Not barefoot
2 Glowing personality?
3 Pretends to cooperate

4 Tortilla chip dip
5 Official language of Kenya
6 Edible tropical tuber
7 Vulnerably positioned
8 Like gymnasts
9 "One of ___ days ..."
15 Handmade
18 Staring dumbfoundedly
19 Like human ears and brains
21 Rival of UPS
23 Sand hill on a beach
24 Audition tape
25 Underworld river

ACROSS

1 Apple computer
5 Ready to hit a homer
10 By a country as a whole
12 "Who's there?" lead-in
13 Winged fruit of a maple or elm
14 Wretchedness
15 Actress Lupino or muckraker Tarbell
16 Prejudice
17 Sid Ceasar sidekick Imogene
19 Prohibit
20 Biceps locale
21 *The Wizard of Oz* scarecrow portrayer Ray
24 Quit bothering
26 Suffer a setback
27 Donkeys
28 Sport-___ (off-road vehicles)

DOWN

1 Writing fluids
2 "Give that ___ cigar!"
3 One of an element's statistics
4 Shrill-sounding insect
5 "Diana" singer Paul
6 Darken in the sun
7 Bursting, as a tire
8 Cut-Rite wax paper company
9 Young 'uns
11 Slimy vegetable
16 *Cat* ___ (Jane Fonda film)
17 ___ halt to (end)
18 Double Stuf cookies
19 Male swine
21 Panhandles
22 Feminine noun suffix
23 Cardinal, carmine, and crimson
25 Neckline shape

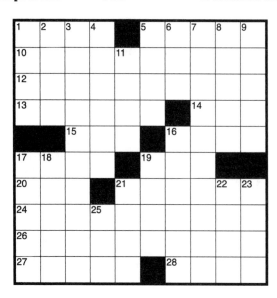

31

ACROSS
1 Private, as thoughts
6 Long narrative
10 "The Wild Swans at ___" (Yeats poem)
11 ___ pro quo (substitute)
12 Improvise
13 River in central Africa
14 Seder soup dumplings
16 Aaron's son and successor to the priesthood
17 Montana State University locale
21 Grimaces, pouts, or sneers

24 Send forth
25 Big blood carrier
26 Actor Green of the *Austin Powers* films
27 Spinning helicopter part
28 Opposed to
29 American flag's 50

DOWN
1 The *"veni"* of *"veni, vidi, vici"*
2 Of a central point
3 *The Prince of Tides* star Nick
4 Queen of England, 1558–1603

5 Long scarves worn by Mexican women
6 Carpet area unit
7 *The Clan of the Cave Bear* novelist Jean
8 Fish's respiratory organ
9 Juice drinks
15 Marketplaces
18 One of the Von Trapp daughters
19 Thespian
20 Gets closer to
21 Plateau's smaller relative
22 "Preach it, pastor!"
23 Catwoman portrayer Eartha

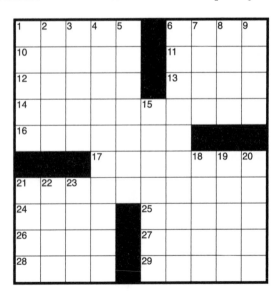

ACROSS
1 Light-skinned
5 Tongue-in-___
10 St. Louis landmark
11 Like some Hindu breathing and posture exercises
12 "See ya!"
13 Boss, in Africa
14 Forked-tailed seabird
15 Lazy person
16 How sports cars are designed
18 Most feral
22 Howard Stern's medium
25 Wised up about
26 *Dynasty* actress Linda

27 ___ about (roughly)
28 Bo of *Bolero*
29 Wields a shovel
30 Don some duds
31 Toy that has its ups and downs

DOWN
1 Almanac contents
2 Israeli prime minister Sharon
3 Concerned comment
4 Beaujolais, Tavel, and Châteauneuf-du-Pape
5 *Moonlighting* star Shepherd

6 Freckle-faced marionette of '50s TV
7 The same, in France
8 Mozart's ___ *kleine Nachtmusik*
9 Discontinued Chrysler design
17 Newsstands
19 Film score composer Morricone
20 Cheap cigar
21 Trunk of the human body
22 Funnyman Foxx
23 Declare to be so
24 Have the guts

33

ACROSS
1 Mexican city opposite El Paso
7 Online info sheet
10 Cling
11 Monkey in *Aladdin*
12 Of a definite quantity
14 Strong glues
15 Wild sea goose
18 Go the distance
19 Remainder
20 Blokes
21 Essentially
23 Period of rivalry between democratic and Communist countries

27 Foot part
28 Track and field Hall-of-Famer Ashford
29 Plane's domain
30 Judged to be

DOWN
1 Traffic tie-up
2 Ulan-___ (Siberian city near Lake Baikal)
3 "Caught ya!"
4 Held a grudge against
5 Spew lava
6 Not even one
7 Name of a pope or a pop singer

8 Most competent
9 Searches
13 Fixed bar upon which wheels rotate, as on a cart
15 Specialized leaves at the base of a flower
16 Captured again
17 Wynonna Judd's sister
20 Tombstone locale
22 Bowled over
24 Massachusetts state tree
25 Kind of bread or whiskey
26 As well as

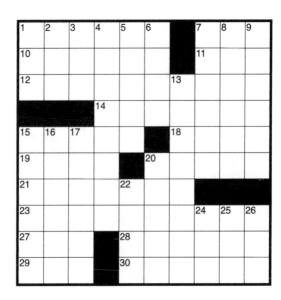

34

ACROSS

1 Jumping-off
   point
5 Poolroom
   triangles
10 Actress ___
   Flynn Boyle
11 ___ Gay (WWII
   bomber)
12 Magazine for
   investors
14 Charged
   particle
15 Pleasant
   paycheck
   surprises
16 Terminus
18 More easy and
   sprightly
21 George's wife on
   The Jeffersons

23 Number between
   due and quattro
24 Stats for a
   pitcher
26 Blacksmith
27 Busily working
28 Voiceless
   consonants, in
   phonetics
29 Casual shirts

DOWN

1 Cow in Borden's
   milk ads
2 Good Will
   Hunting star Matt
3 One helping to
   decide whether
   an alleged
   criminal should
   stand trial

4 Cochlea
   locale
5 Stayed
6 Apply holy
   oil to
7 Make up
8 Twittering
   Machine artist
   Paul
9 Puts into words
13 Pants
17 Caused hurt to
19 Tennessee
   ___ Ford
20 Takes a
   breather
21 Not as much
22 Honolulu's
   island
25 Maze-running
   rodent

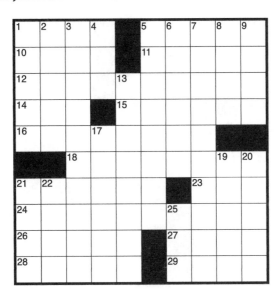

39

ACROSS
1 Agree
7 Outlaw
10 Form a thought
11 Actress Gardner
12 Borderline cuisine?
13 Bro or sis
14 Acid-alcohol compound
15 Tower on a farm
16 Where a semi driver sits
18 Made a rustling sound
20 Pottery oven
21 Spine-tingling
24 Ore-___ (big name in frozen fries)
25 Ron of the NBA
26 Notes to follow do
27 Isn't truthful with
28 Explosive stuff
29 Part of VIP

DOWN
1 Quote
2 Praise-filled poems
3 Penultimate
4 *Jerry Maguire* director Crowe
5 Womb
6 *Oedipus* ___
7 No-frills item of women's wear
8 St. Theresa's home
9 Tycoon
15 Bloodsucking pest, slangily
17 Stevie Wonder's "My ___ Amour"
18 Pantsuit alternative
19 Dilate, as pupils
22 What a colon means in an analogy
23 British school founded in 1440
25 Swiss peak

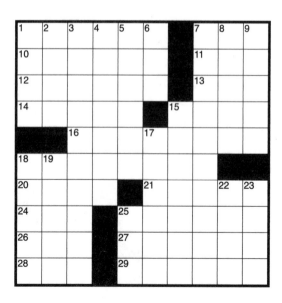

36

ACROSS

1 Pink gemstone material
11 Has more troops than, e.g.
12 Newspapers, magazines, etc., related to a specific profession
13 High-arcing tennis shot
14 Airhead
15 Cubic meters
18 ___ gestae (deeds)
19 Overdramatic actor
20 Shutterbug's need
22 Airport guesses: Abbr.
24 Carpet sweeper, for short
25 Rapid succession of tapping sounds
29 Deterrents
30 OK'd

DOWN

1 Decay
2 "They're playing ___ song"
3 Deadlocks
4 Biblical witch's home
5 Canadian province
6 Steak-___ (brand in the frozen section)
7 Under the covers
8 Changed the course of
9 More hackneyed
10 One of the Gabor sisters
15 Tibetan mountain-climbing guide
16 Turkish tribesmen
17 Idiot ___
21 Dull photo finish
23 Rescue
26 Gymnast's dream score
27 Gallery exhibits
28 General ___'s chicken

ACROSS

1 Badgers
5 Jumble
10 *A Streetcar Named Desire* director Kazan
11 Senseless
12 Not in equilibrium
14 Excursion along a forest trail
15 Highest points
16 With hands on hips and elbows bent outward
20 Digital watch reading
25 Agree to cease fire
26 "There's ___ every crowd!"
27 Vegetable in gumbo soup
28 Some German cars
29 Look intently

DOWN

1 Bright light on Broadway
2 Italian sports car, for short
3 Natural talent
4 Actor in *The Jungle Book* and *Elephant Boy*
5 Highway distance marker
6 Flabbergasted
7 Prescription antianxiety drug
8 Mother's brother
9 Steals a glance
13 Persian Gulf residents
16 Company that merged with Reynolds Metals in 2000
17 *The Matrix* star Reeves
18 Sat doing nothing
19 Caesar's 1,552
21 Shore up
22 Skywalker or Perry
23 $\frac{1}{640}$ of a square mile
24 Decade division

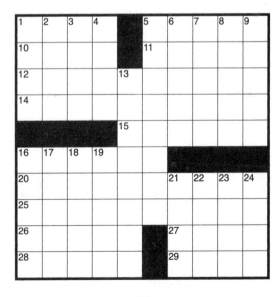

ACROSS

1 Sevens-through-aces card game
5 *Broom-___* (comic strip)
10 Bust by the fuzz
12 Motel chain
13 Sunny disposition
14 Curry favor with, with "to"
15 Ethiopian's neighbor to the east
20 Minimum wages, e.g.
24 Made with no artificial ingredients
25 CBS Internet site with game coverage
26 Cone-shaped tent
27 Mouth off to

DOWN

1 Little particle
2 Japanese seaport on Shikoku island
3 First-aid plants
4 Points on a fork
5 Choppers' landing areas
6 Press out wrinkles
7 Put on cargo
8 Uses a trowel
9 Fruit-flavored drinks
11 Emit vivid flashes of light
16 Knocks around
17 Skylit central courts
18 Tilts
19 Molokai, Capri, and Skye
20 Strong, woody fiber
21 Swiss mountain, in Marseilles
22 Food in a hog trough
23 Regarding

ACROSS

1 Fox skit show
6 Take ___ view of (frown on)
10 Potato-growing state
11 *Sleepless in Seattle* director Ephron
12 Original concepts
14 Kids' construction toy
15 Burst ___ the scene
16 San Francisco's ___ Hill
17 Sound of deliberation
19 Prefix with hertz or corporation
22 One who really hates

25 Jim Carrey or Steve Martin, e.g.
26 Gabor and Perón
27 The Beatles' "___ Woman"
28 Punctuation mark longer than a hyphen
29 "___ mud in your eye!"

DOWN

1 *Rebel Without a Cause* actor Sal
2 Decorate
3 Founder of Wendy's restaurant
4 Early '90s crime drama starring Michael Chiklis

5 Battery unit
6 Euripides tragedy about Hector's wife
7 Shows improvement
8 *"Dies ___"* (Requiem Mass hymn)
9 Sail supporter
13 Charged atom
18 Talk-show guest's lapel attachment, for short
20 Swan's cousin
21 Rich tapestry
22 Did extremely well on, as a test
23 Sci-fi novelist Ben
24 Crosby, Stills & ___

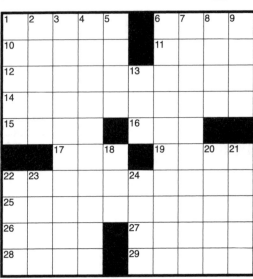

44

40

ACROSS

1 River in central Germany
5 Like a big brother, agewise
10 Tibetan monk
11 Because of
12 Temporarily suspended
14 Karate's cousin
15 Homes
16 Sea, to Henri
19 That lady
20 Title differently
22 Separated, as a pair of oxen
23 Sentimental do-gooders
26 Small bay
27 *Desperate Housewives* role
28 Take another stab at
29 Fa-ti linkup

DOWN

1 *The Lord of the Rings* star Wood
2 Europe's second longest river
3 Key with four sharps
4 Fanatically zealous
5 Long, adventure-filled journeys
6 Hawaiian cookout
7 Jungle shelter
8 And so on: Abbr.
9 Wade's court rival
13 There's no end to it
16 Manage somehow
17 TV chef who "kicks it up"
18 Moses parted it
21 Lecture jottings
22 Exploitative type
23 Knight's title
24 Dollar bill
25 Classic diner sandwich

1	2	3	4		5	6	7	8	9
10					11				
12			13						
14									
15						16	17	18	
19				20		21			
			22						
23	24	25							
26						27			
28						29			

41

ACROSS
1 Ocean motion
5 *Star Wars* baddie ___ Vader
10 No later than
12 China's Cultural Revolution leaders
13 Pantry pest
14 Word after brow, breast, or egg
15 Nintendo rival
17 Rocker Ocasek or wrestler Flair
18 Number like "first" or "second": Abbr.
20 Tattered cloths
23 Supreme Court justice Antonin
26 Spoon-bender Geller
27 Wrote in uncapitalized letters
29 Citrus rind
30 Check recipient
31 Italy's Villa d'___

DOWN
1 Colosseum garments
2 Pointless
3 Words before "We'll be right back!"
4 Unit of work
5 Put off until later
6 Brief romance
7 Underlying sources
8 Faithful
9 Mr., in Munich
11 Singer Seger
16 Dahl of Hollywood
19 Funeral song
21 Say "Hey!" to
22 Move like a crab
23 Unappetizing food
24 Actress Witherspoon
25 High card
28 Gibbon or gorilla

42

ACROSS

1 Sci-fi abductor
11 Very minor sin
12 Opposed to Russia
13 Minestrone ingredients
14 Puccini opera about a diva
15 Dads
18 Photographer's carrying case
22 Not open to doubt
24 Irish elf
25 Tried out a toy or a game before it's marketed

DOWN

1 Hot-tub hangout
2 *Sweet and Lowdown* star Sean
3 Official records
4 Nero's 204
5 Sitting duck
6 Topping for chipotle peppers
7 Resides
8 ___ artery (aorta offshoot)
9 Verdugo of film

10 Have-___ (poor people)
15 Discussion group
16 Brazilian state whose capital is Macapá
17 *Friends* costar Matthew
18 Cosby's *I Spy* costar Robert
19 Scrooge's exclamations
20 As blind as ___
21 Elmer's product
23 Terminate

1	2	3	4	5	6	7	8	9	10
11									
12									
	13								
			14						
	15	16	17						
18					19	20	21		
22									23
24									
25									

10-Minute
Crosswords

43

ACROSS

1 Very, very ancient
16 Crown prince, e.g.
17 Average imbiber
18 ___-Cat (winter vehicle)
19 Suffix with serpent
20 Hankering
21 "___ a sin to tell a lie"
22 Reuters rival
23 Corporate VIP
25 Moisturizes
29 Wither
33 Lambs' mothers
34 Implied
36 Former Italian currency
37 Gold coating
38 Rest
39 Sing like Ella
40 On the briny
41 Composer of "The Liberty Bell"
43 Facilitate
44 Himalayan guides
46 Arranger
48 Highland hat
49 El ___ (Spanish hero)
50 So-so grade
53 Republican's letters
55 Balloon fill
56 TV's "___ Na Na"
59 Passover food
63 Literary figure?
64 Dry runs

DOWN

1 Resistance units
2 Ponce de ___
3 Queen of Carthage
4 "We ___ the World"
5 Band
6 Complainer's activity
7 Suffix with cigar
8 English article
9 Actress Lamarr
10 Central Netherlands city
11 Black eye
12 It may follow directions
13 Norse deity
14 Work without ___ (take risks)
15 Towel word
22 Presumptuous person
24 Castor bean, for one
25 "L'Absinthe" painter Edgar
26 "Make ___!" (birthday request)
27 Riotous fight
28 Flies alone
29 Authority
30 Reverend
31 Rub out
32 Afterwards
35 Sigma follower
41 Urn
42 Region of Greece
45 Heathens
47 Expel from practice, as a lawyer
50 Prompted
51 ___'acte
52 Gen. Robt. ___
54 Brazilian soccer legend
55 "American Gigolo" actor Richard
56 Nintendo competitor
57 Lobby
58 Fruit drinks
60 Sounds of uncertainty
61 Ultimate degree
62 Hosp. workers

50

44

ACROSS

1 Tags
7 By the time
15 It works like a charm
16 Most showery
17 Hubbub
18 Deer's companion, in song
19 Fix, as a jacket
20 O.T. book
21 Diarist Anaïs
22 Obliterates
23 Bookie's place: Abbr.
24 He cracks down on crack
25 Social outcasts
26 Earnings
27 Provo's place
28 Passover meal
30 Neck growth
31 Imitation
35 Type of boom
37 Fast food sandwiches, briefly
38 Peek follower
39 ___ Ark

41 Nevada city
42 Air conditioner unit: Abbr.
43 Horrify
48 Clock sound
49 Hairy Addams Family cousin
50 Herb of the mint family
51 Wight or Man: Abbr.
52 Day-___ paints
53 Singer Shania and family
54 Nemo's submarine
57 Congenital
58 Roundabout
59 Hunting dog
60 Furtive
61 Ford flops

DOWN

1 Hardy's partner in comedy
2 Current unit
3 Plain-woven fabric
4 Fictional Plaza Hotel brat

5 Some horseshoe throws
6 Underlines
7 Coach Parseghian
8 Places of recovery
9 Is located near
10 Draft stratus
11 Alaska export
12 Baby-related
13 Hopeful one
14 Bad smells
23 Unfold
24 Feeling no pain
29 "Hands off!"
31 007's drinks
32 Deferential
33 Bring to a close
34 Eccentric sort
36 Castigate
40 Engendered
42 Soldier's lodging
44 Factories
45 Fly
46 Door beam
47 Scanner lights
52 "It's a ___!"
55 Aunt, in Aragón
56 Hog's home

45

ACROSS
1 Oceangoing
10 Voting places
15 Crocodile's cousin
16 Heep of fiction
17 Private conversation
18 Tiny amount
19 Dangerous bacteria
20 Tilly or Ryan
21 Exhausted
22 Discovery of Watson and Crick
24 ___ rouge (red wine)
25 Soak (up)
28 Peter and Paul: Abbr.
30 Marshland
31 "___ been working on the railroad ..."
34 Pullers of heavy loads
38 Hot climate necessities
39 Chickening out
40 Chemical ending
41 "Nightmare on ___ Street"
42 Lush
43 Avery or Ritter
44 U-turn from NNW

45 Rangers' org.
47 "___ What You Did Last Summer" (1998 movie)
50 Mauna ___
53 Go with the beau
57 Abu ___
58 Literally "dear mother"
60 Supporter of the arts?
61 Putting down
62 Tangle
63 Jambs

DOWN
1 Overfill
2 AC or DC: Abbr.
3 Choir voice
4 Playing area
5 Forcibly
6 Informer
7 Particular
8 Memo
9 Olympic diver Louganis
10 Making famous, in a way
11 Senator Hatch
12 Prevaricator
13 Put punch in the punch
14 Outbuilding
23 Stimulated
24 Deer meat

25 Unoriginal
26 Rigel's constellation
27 Analyze grammatically
29 ___ and Gomorrah
30 Celebrates
31 Like argon or krypton
32 Pep
33 County near London
35 201, to Caesar
36 Trent Reznor's group, for short
37 Suffix with Ernest
44 Clear-headed
46 South American plain
47 Bad time for Caesar
48 Aga ___
49 Apollo org.
50 Actress Cheryl of "Charlie's Angels"
51 Old name for margarine
52 Shot and shells
54 Redding of R&B
55 Closely confined, with "up"
56 Energy units
59 ___ Lingus (Irish carrier)

46

ACROSS
1 Rued the workout
6 Prickly plants
11 Soft food for infants
14 Saltwater
15 New York city
16 Cell material
17 It comes from the heart
18 Spotted pattern
20 Puppet Mortimer
21 Christmas seasons
22 "Hark! the ___ ..."
24 Cheadle of "Ocean's Twelve"
25 Father
26 Combustible heap
28 Cry of dismay
29 Idiot boxes
32 Old-fashioned clothes presser
36 Fever reading
37 "___-la-la!"
38 Ape
39 Ostrich relative
40 Suffix with pay
41 Cartoon partner of Boris

42 Concorde, e.g.
43 Enticements
45 Teachers' favorites
47 "... ___ a man with seven ..."
48 Score units: Abbr.
51 Cane material
55 Peach relative
58 Body of art?
59 "Myra Breckinridge" author
60 Filled with wonder
61 Numero ___
62 ___ Mountains (Arkansas hills)
63 Soldier's decoration
64 Ginger
65 Water sources
66 Blissful places

DOWN
1 Embarrass
2 Hag
3 Boss, at times
4 Catch in a snare
5 Sloth and avarice, e.g.
6 Reproduction
7 Vocally

8 Viola's big brother
9 Swiped
10 ___ the kill
11 Child stars
12 Reception areas
13 Lost consciousness
19 Spoon's companion
23 Play
27 Fix copy
28 Individually
29 Installing machinery
30 Encyclopedia opener
31 Work as a tenant farmer
33 "Make ___ double!"
34 Coarse file
35 Extra
44 Suffix with major
46 Threw rocks at
48 Value highly
49 Type of bore or basin
50 Tangle
52 Barter
53 Nile dam
54 Playwright Coward et al.
56 Swear
57 Part of BPOE

47

ACROSS
1 In the style of
4 Tear-jerking
11 Army rank: Abbr.
14 Nothing
15 Better built
16 Ms. Gabor
17 Neat
20 Souvenir
21 Wearing away
22 Sunday assent
23 Powdery starch
24 Stripling
25 St. Louis footballer
28 Sounds of surprise
31 X rating?
32 Ask for service, in a way
36 Gilbert and Sullivan works
37 Christmas fruit
43 "___ Haw"
44 Was in session
45 U-turn from SSW
46 John in Scotland
47 Son of Aphrodite
49 Razor brand
50 Split ingredients
54 Witty saying
57 Handicapped

59 "Nonsense!"
60 Worry
61 ___ Aviv
62 Rap's Dr. ___
63 Truck drivers?
64 Pluralizing letter

DOWN
1 Zoo residents
2 Football position
3 City near San Francisco
4 Channel with lots of games
5 Shed feathers
6 Prefix with resin or margarine
7 Point
8 "Each Dawn ___" (1939 movie)
9 Swerve
10 Smack or switch ender
11 Settle a dispute
12 Retaliator
13 Specialized vocabularies
18 Sword vanquisher
19 Map abbreviations
25 Strong cords

26 The end of ___
27 Deserve
28 Frequently
29 Make a pass at
30 Trap
33 Collectible juice cap
34 Washington pol.
35 Juliette Gordon Low's gp.
37 ___ of Avon (Shakespeare)
38 Ventilator, of a sort
39 Maternity ward arrival
40 Sodium ___ (food preservative)
41 Carports
42 Tooth coatings
48 Down in the dumps
49 Bond or Smart: Abbr.
51 Courteous
52 "Unto us ___ is given ..."
53 Chorused
54 Level
55 Whittle
56 Taverns
58 601, to Ovid

48

ACROSS
1 Sail supporter
5 Weapons merchant
15 Suffix with usher
16 Property
17 Let it stand, in printing
18 Nastassja Kinski movie of 1984
19 Bog
20 Zool., e.g.
21 Dole, with "out"
22 It's big in Sicily
23 Orb
26 Queue after Q
27 Peewee
28 ___ Maria
29 Sundown, in poesy
31 Notion, in Nancy
32 "___ Well That Ends Well"
34 Swift swallows
38 Gusto
39 High-pitched barks
41 Smell
42 Big Bertha's birthplace
44 Male horse
45 Rani's attire
46 Message in a bottle, maybe
48 Wedding page word

49 Work on the galleys
50 Mao ___-tung
53 Amalgamation
55 Thin fog
56 Steering mechanism
58 Aye's opposite
59 Suffix with appear
60 Record-keepers
64 Composer Stravinsky
65 One-sided
66 Hoodwink
67 Check alternative
68 Went like the wind

DOWN
1 Induce hypnosis in
2 Dispositions
3 Austere quality
4 Intimate chats
5 Dada artist Jean ___
6 Actor Stephen of "Citizen X"
7 Freight train assembly area
8 Pizza serving
9 Want
10 Boston clock setting: Abbr.

11 "Up and ___!"
12 Less rigid
13 States, in Soissons
14 Bowling alley button
23 Remain
24 Heaps
25 Brain reading: Abbr.
30 Nannies
33 Shopping indulgence
35 Preparing the way
36 Submarine's "eye"
37 Glided rapidly
40 Oracle
43 Henri or Yves, e.g.
47 ___ jail (incarcerated)
50 Make a rhythmic sound
51 "___ evil ..."
52 Illinois city on the Fox River
54 Less common
57 Distance measure
61 Pronounce
62 "Norma ___"
63 Type of camera: Abbr.

49

ACROSS
1 Money-mobile
11 Wife of Osiris
15 Enforced isolation
16 "Alas!"
17 Not absorbed, as food
18 Grape ___ (Radar's drink)
19 Succulent plants
20 Armed conflict
22 Skaggs of rock
23 Chattanooga's state: Abbr.
24 Pacino et al.
27 "Open ___!"
29 Ain't correct?
30 Squad
32 Lion's growth
33 Civil War letters
34 Implying
36 Warm underwear
37 Calibrated precisely
38 Energy
41 Complaint
42 Let one's ___ down (relax)
43 Florence's river
44 Aromatic herb
46 Born

47 Decays
48 Rocket's path
49 VCR button
51 Rescues
52 Follow closely
54 Extremely arid
58 Periodic table abbreviation
59 Clapton and Hendrix, e.g.
60 Toy building block brand
61 Gives details

DOWN
1 Water-related
2 Without scoring, in baseball
3 "Like a Virgin" singer
4 Christie's "Murder on the ___ Express"
5 Cleaning cloths
6 Vane dir.
7 Withdrawal symptoms, for short
8 Op ___ (footnote abbr.)
9 Once more
10 ___ a beet

11 Holm or Hendry
12 The whole ___ (everything)
13 "Hi, honey, ___!"
14 Grab
21 Jog one's memory
24 Repent
25 Duration
26 Puerto Rico's capital
28 Without
31 Unification Church member
34 Bestow
35 "Finished!"
36 Mortgage
37 Swordplay
38 University administrator
39 Informal alliance
40 Have
41 Chew out
43 Saudi ___
44 Deadly
45 Rocky shelf
50 Gist
51 Rani's robe
53 London privy
55 Puppy's sound
56 ___ glance
57 Posed

50

ACROSS

1 Designated
7 Wander aimlessly, with "about"
10 "Where's the cheek that ___ not fade ...": Keats
14 Breathe out
15 "___ had my way ..."
16 Fencing sword
17 Sour in taste
18 Listens
20 Capitol Hill body
21 Skating surfaces
22 Gold or lithium, e.g.
24 "This ___ test ..."
25 Sneaky laugh
26 Seer's card
28 "Count me out!"
29 Take ___ at (try)
34 He's a real doll
35 Overwhelming defeats
36 Smut
37 Zeta follower
38 Passageway
39 Giving great service?
40 Small quantity

41 Actress Garson
42 Fully developed
43 George Burns comedy of 1977
45 Use a shuttle
46 Regret
47 Brings down, emotionally
53 Passing quickly, as time
56 Average
57 Two-wheeled passenger cart
58 Rut
59 Will-___-wisp
60 Spasm
61 Officially entered
62 Untidy state
63 One-time link
64 Atelier props

DOWN

1 Rib
2 Surpass
3 Major European river
4 "___, I'm Adam"
5 High-class
6 Appropriate
7 Leslie Caron movie of 1958
8 Devotees
9 Sell off, as holding
10 Mr. Arnaz

11 Informal party
12 Mother's whistler?
13 Baseball's Orel
19 Chapter
23 Bite, so to speak
27 Label anew
28 Black, to Blanche
29 Besides
30 Prominent person in the party scene
31 Three-panel artworks
32 Baxter or Boleyn
33 Wet spongy ground
35 Joplin composition
43 "There ___ be a law!"
44 Hang freely
46 Essential hospital workers: Abbr.
48 Andrea ___ (famous ship)
49 Waste matter
50 Chew the scenery
51 Belly button
52 Huskies' tows
54 Eisenhower et al.
55 Shelter-providing org.

51

ACROSS
1 Wharf
5 Horn or rattle, e.g.
15 Eclectic magazine
16 It may be split
17 Actor McKellen et al.
18 Ice cream variety
19 Stripper's garment
21 A and B in D.C.: Abbr.
22 Wield a blue pencil
23 Mined material
25 180° from WNW
26 '60s political gp.
29 Colony member
31 Engine additive letters
32 Here, in Montreal
35 '80s White House resident
39 Feel jealousy
40 Richard Harris movie of 1970
41 "Norma ___"
42 Parseghian of coaching fame
43 Sign of summer
44 Poivre companion
45 "___ Robinson"
46 Total amount

48 "Exit, pursued by ___": Shakespeare
51 Tight spot
54 Destroys
58 Horror classic of 1985
61 Get one's ___ (annoy)
62 Goal, of a sort
63 Inquisitive
64 Ensued
65 Visa alternative, briefly

DOWN
1 Throw in the towel
2 State with many Mormons
3 ___ domini
4 Type of question
5 Diarist Anaïs
6 Change from a five
7 "___ first you don't succeed ..."
8 Drinks slowly
9 Brian of Roxy Music
10 Speedometer reading
11 "Once upon ___ ..."
12 Small hawk
13 Author Hunter

14 Tear
20 Wheat transporter
24 Pleases
25 Internet stock transactions
26 Lance
27 Play
28 Botanical bristles
30 Electrical inventor Nikola
31 Iron alloy
32 Stravinsky and Sikorsky
33 ___ and effect
34 Pentium producer
36 Dad's boy
37 Canucks' org.
38 From ___ Z
45 Dog's affliction
47 ___ Carta
48 They may be fine
49 Boyfriend
50 Tombstone name
51 Tire
52 ___ impasse (deadlocked)
53 Speck
55 Move rapidly
56 Simplicity
57 Charon's river
59 Rock video network
60 Crimson

52

ACROSS

1 Expel from practice, as a lawyer
7 Algonquian language
13 Submissions
15 Miles and Vaughan
16 Baby carriage
18 Uplifts
19 Popular cookies
20 Loser to DDE
22 Actor Milo
23 Told tales
24 Reckless
26 Tarzan portrayer Ron
27 Opera opener, often
28 Satanic
29 Subdue
30 Command to a horse
31 Impudent talk
35 LAX listings
36 Actor in "The A-Team"
37 Baseball's Matty
38 Bureau: Abbr.
39 Averages
41 Revolved quickly
42 Domestic servant
43 Composer Jerome
44 Stick out
47 ___-weensy
48 Opposing
49 "And thereby hangs ___": Shakespeare
51 Police officer's rank: Abbr.
52 Actor Hawke
53 Buccaneer
55 Free
57 Oaks, in a nutshell
58 Vacation spots
59 NYSE alternative
60 French film festival site

DOWN

1 Ravaged
2 Elaborate
3 AAA handout
4 Most contemplative
5 Feels feverish
6 Fam. tree member
7 Ending with verb
8 Old heap
9 Some retirement accts.
10 Swim
11 Roulette spinner
12 Test
14 Marine polyps
17 Distracting fish?
21 Pack leader
24 Beer glass
25 Swiss peak
31 Canadian city
32 Powerful Swiss instrument
33 Lemon's attribute
34 Gaiety
39 Name-dropper's word?
40 Cunning
42 Sicilian volcano
44 Osaka's land
45 Central New York city
46 Poi plants
50 Hog fat
52 Fictional lioness
54 Title of respect: Abbr.
56 Gumshoe

ACROSS

1 Popular '80s car
8 Lays waste to
15 Outdoor
16 Divorcé's payment
17 Wed anew
18 Sirius, familiarly
19 Epoch
20 Hitchcock classic of 1958
22 "___ on parle Français"
23 Ski jacket
25 Tic-tac-toe win, maybe
26 ___-car
28 Aleutian island
29 Stags
31 Tommy's carbine
32 "___ End Girls" (Pet Shop Boys hit)
33 Good ___ (restored)
34 Lays down the lawn
35 Like old bread
36 Radial part
40 Increased
41 Take ___ view of (regard poorly)
45 Slangy suffix
46 "___-porridge hot ..."
47 Verne captain
48 Enormous
50 Joan of ___
51 "Encore!"
52 Drug also known as acid
53 Dismissed
56 Rehab shakes
57 Judo relative
59 Rainfall sound
61 Most dry
62 Lift
63 Sucking fishes
64 More tranquil

DOWN

1 Cat's "hand"
2 Perform surgery
3 Comments
4 Double helix letters
5 Insect stage
6 Fatigue
7 Planters products
8 Astronomers' dishes
9 Sleep like ___
10 Vim's partner
11 Morning periods, for short
12 Became involved with
13 Brought into law
14 Damascus natives
21 Ripped to pieces
24 "Krazy ___"
27 Frowned-upon feminizing suffix
29 Brings before a magistrate
30 Stockholm native
36 Protective glass cover
37 Takeout sign?
38 Conrad classic
39 Dress nattily, with "up"
41 Movie director ___ Lee
42 Poker-faced
43 Copy
44 Mythical Loch Ness creature
49 Fragrant compound
51 Subsequently
54 It, in Italy
55 Dossier
58 Altar agreement
60 "___ Maria"

54

ACROSS

1 The, to a grammarian
16 Minutia
17 Occupied community
18 Badminton barriers
19 Prefix with thermal
20 Singer Loretta
21 Mideast org.
23 Fleet gp.
26 Aviator Earhart
30 Revolutionary groups
35 City or sausage
37 Oberon's wife
38 White keys, on a piano
39 Thinks logically
40 Goes
41 Entrails
42 Once, once
43 Bright and pleasant
44 ___ de plume
46 Oolong or pekoe
47 "Horton Hears ___" (Dr. Seuss book)
51 "May ___ of service?"
53 Aspiring GP's exam

57 Royal couple of the '80s
62 Summer cooler
63 Look sharp

DOWN

1 Bruce or Laura
2 Part of a CSA signature
3 Quick
4 Graceful wading bird
5 Silent assent
6 Wrath
7 Dance that takes two
8 Diminutive suffix
9 Vowel sequence
10 Vitamin bottle abbreviation
11 ___ Aviv
12 Slanted type: Abbr.
13 Actor Grant
14 Legal property claim
15 Panache
21 Blast furnace fodder
22 Drag strip section
24 Biology or chemistry
25 Actress Henstridge of "Species 2"

26 Tolerate
27 Chess player, at times
28 Skip a big wedding
29 Marine navigation system
31 Musical Count
32 Battery terminal
33 Passenger ship
34 Full of lip
36 Beast of burden
37 Three: Prefix
45 Perform improperly
46 Agent's take, often
47 Military sch.
48 Spinning sound
49 Tortoise's rival
50 Monsters in "The Lord of the Rings"
52 Cheese in a mousetrap, e.g.
53 Short skirt
54 Brother of Abel
55 Green Gables girl
56 Small labels
58 ___ Angeles
59 Suffix with differ
60 Expire
61 Imus of radio

55

ACROSS

1 Eva's sister
7 Raised road
15 Involve
16 Gangster known as "Scarface"
17 Happen to, old-style
18 Sofia's nation
19 Parents, e.g.
21 West of "Sextette"
22 Metric distance measures: Abbr.
23 Handcuffed one
25 Help with a heist
26 Test
30 TV's "Remington ___"
36 Forestalls
39 Schwarzenegger comedy of 1990
41 Muncie native
42 Wheezing disorder
43 Gives
45 Madcap
47 Gun attachment
54 U.K. language
55 Suntan spoiler
58 Pasta choice
59 Most mistrustful
62 Abounded
63 Vex
64 Queued up

65 Accelerator, familiarly
66 Earnhardt's milieu

DOWN

1 Black-and-white beast
2 Express contempt
3 Rose oil
4 The Democratic Republic of the Congo, formerly
5 Facets
6 Red state?
7 Bus alternative
8 Grad
9 Bruins' letters
10 Guru
11 Smog watchdogs: Abbr.
12 Carpenter's table
13 Japanese cartoon genre
14 Brewer's need
20 "What did I tell you?"
24 Enlarges
25 Regarding
27 Part of ETA
28 Introduction to physics?

29 Actor/singer Burl
30 Tackle moguls
31 Stannary metal
32 Jeopardizes
33 Enlighten
34 Turn over a new ___ (reform)
35 Puzzle cube inventor Rubik
37 Mr. Brokaw
38 Springs for a holiday?
40 Needlefish
44 Lancelot's title
45 Woody Allen pseudo-documentary of 1983
46 The end of ___
48 Caesar's tongue
49 "... not ___ mouse"
50 Physicist Bohr
51 Funny fellow
52 Actress Verdugo
53 Equestrian
55 Take the bait
56 Interpret
57 Nick and Nora's dog
60 Lacerate
61 Bell's invention: Abbr.

74

56

ACROSS
1 Big name in coffee shops
10 Goldman's partner
15 Elite graduating list
16 Hate
17 One who gives approval, perhaps
18 Cat calls
19 ___ de plume
20 "Waiting for the Robert ___"
21 Blueprint item, briefly
22 Duo
24 Gray's subject
27 Pooch
28 Desolate
31 52, to Caesar
32 Metal-bearing minerals
33 Sharp
34 Stinging insect
35 High hairstyle
36 Singer-actress Jennifer
37 "Take ___ from me ..."
38 Roll's partner
39 Henri's brother
40 Heredity unit
41 Code-cracking org.

42 Loved ones
43 Being, to Brutus
44 Grave
46 Very dry, as champagne
47 Russian ruler, once
48 Neck part
51 U.S. gun gp.
53 Sunday singers
55 Became less intoxicated
57 Blessings
58 Show too much emotion
59 Char
60 Flamenco clickers

DOWN
1 Climb awkwardly, with "up"
2 Without aim
3 Short, maybe
4 "Hogwash!"
5 Pipe type
6 River to the Caspian
7 ___ slaw
8 Swiss painter Paul
9 Camera type: Abbr.

10 Asian skiff
11 Red as ___
12 Malt shop purchase
13 "In what way?"
14 Elders: Abbr.
21 Reacts to pollen, perhaps
23 "Don't worry!"
24 Blood vessel
25 Teach improperly
26 "Eureka!"
27 Grieves
28 British prime minister, 1902–05
29 Oaks-to-be
30 Indian coin
34 Bet
42 Having a raucous voice
45 "Of Thee ___"
46 Baseball's Yogi
48 PBS science show
49 Lincoln and Vigoda
50 Saucy
52 Suites: Abbr.
53 "Survivor" network
54 ___ polloi
55 Assn.
56 Hallow ending

57

ACROSS
1 ___ Hari
5 Weeps
9 Male athletes, slangily
14 "Put yer hands in the air!"
16 Kitchen garment
17 Tibetan VIP
18 "Cool!"
19 Senior citizen
20 Colorful arc
22 Precipitates rain and snow
23 Good Queen ___
24 Patina
25 Baseball glove
29 JoBeth Williams/ Tom Conti movie of 1984
36 Neil Simon movie of 1978
37 Advance, as in battle
38 Medium-length run
39 Grade
40 Does something
41 Idiots
47 Galileo ___
51 Amasses
52 Live
53 Fruity quaff

55 National ___ Association
56 Homesick
57 Poly ending
58 Adjusts, as an alarm
59 Gets the picture

DOWN
1 Computer operating system
2 Ever
3 Spanish diacritical mark
4 Make ___ for (argue the merits of)
5 Monica of tennis
6 Actor Epps
7 Vagabond
8 "Buddy, can you ___?"
9 Singer Joplin
10 Candid
11 Grouch
12 Japanese stringed instrument
13 Winter forecast
15 Eartha of song
21 Off course
23 Easter headgear

24 Lapel flowers
25 Hawaii neighbor
26 "___ the Mood for Love"
27 Head, in Haiti
28 Very, in Versailles
29 Bank offering: Abbr.
30 Female horse
31 North Carolina college
32 Take chances
33 No ___, ands, or buts
34 Put pressure on
35 Immigrants course: Abbr.
40 Change
41 Money makers
42 Gymnast Korbut
43 Highland dances
44 Early Missourian
45 Skin flick
46 Eyeglasses
47 "Runaway Bride" costar Richard
48 Turning point
49 English elevator
50 ___ of Wight
51 Yesteryear
54 Anonymous Richard

58

ACROSS

1 Formerly, once
5 Flooded
10 Hot Pontiac cars of yore
14 Fortuneteller
15 Bert's buddy on "Sesame Street"
16 Make ___ for it (flee)
17 Father, in France
18 Muscle
19 Columnist Barrett
20 Actress Sosnovska
21 Word before ear or drum
22 "Get your head down!"
23 Grape center
24 Davis of "Thelma & Louise"
26 Olympian's sword
27 Actress Lupino et al.
28 Sweet quality
30 Shade
31 Large copier?
32 Long focus setting: Abbr.
33 Johnny-___-spot
35 Letters on a Cardinal's cap

37 Noah's Ark measure
41 Easter gift
43 Yang's partner
45 San ___ (Italian resort)
46 Exact duplicate
50 Neck area
51 Black-and-white cookie
52 Intermission
53 Cool-sounding rapper?
54 Pond plant
55 '80s TV tough guy
56 Commotion
57 Bender
58 Protection
60 Apartment
61 Author Bagnold
62 Cease-fire
63 Former Attorney General Janet
64 Cubbyholes?
65 Sri ___
66 Boundary

DOWN

1 Hockey legend Phil
2 Landed, as a fish
3 Corporal's superior
4 Goes on stage
5 Loser to DDE

6 Reports
7 Betty Hutton musical of 1950
8 Earth color
9 Chop down
10 Lawn chairs, etc.
11 Group of actors
12 Pound parts
13 Ladders' companions in a game
24 Annual cookie vendors: Abbr.
25 Actress Meyers
29 Company letters?
34 Swelled head
36 Cosmetic case item
38 Shone, as a lighthouse
39 Causing a jam
40 One way to stand
42 Important economic statistic: Abbr.
44 TV's "Science Guy" Bill
46 Plated
47 Actress Dahl
48 Find
49 Kodak item
58 Iceland's ocean: Abbr.
59 Where the buoys and gulls are

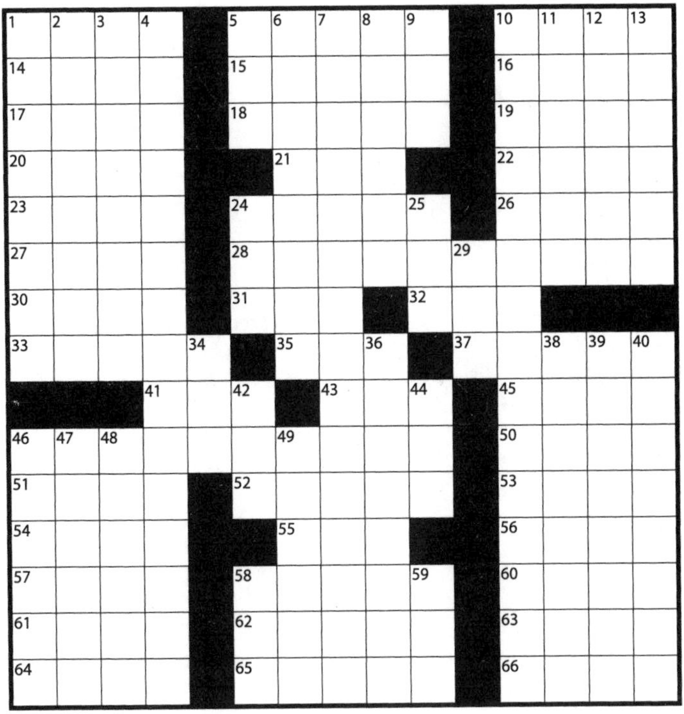

59

ACROSS

1 Business person's tote
12 Large Australian bird
15 Organized
16 One of the Bobbsey twins
17 Printers' assistants
18 Name
19 Capital of Italia
20 A.A. Milne donkey
22 Greek vowel
23 Race
28 Sophia of "Man of La Mancha"
29 Carrier out of Stockholm
30 Supermarket pathway
31 Secondhand
32 Former Air France jet
33 Get closer to sunset
34 Small warblers
35 ___ of Assisi
37 Helps a hood
40 Negatively charged atom
41 "60 Minutes" network
44 Highway section
45 "Tiny Bubbles" singer
46 Celestial altar
47 Change
49 Toronto footballers, familiarly
50 "Spare the ___ ..."
51 Outwardly curved limb
53 Cut, as a lawn
54 Black cuckoo
55 Mickey's cartoon girlfriend
61 Guys
62 Large web-footed sea birds
63 Yes vote
64 Leaders, of a sort

DOWN

1 Female thespian
2 Supras and Corollas
3 Yard support
4 Expanse
5 Music-lovers' purchases, briefly
6 Rush
7 Tolkien creature
8 Jaguar, e.g.
9 Had supper
10 Dry and withered
11 Ford failure
12 Certify
13 O'Hara of "Jamaica Inn"
14 Straightens out
21 "___ truly ..."
23 Tars
24 Singer Edith
25 Erik of "CHiPs"
26 Ms. Roosevelt
27 Inhabiting a lair
34 They can't pass the bar
35 Girder metal
36 Salmon variety
37 Mobile's state
38 "Bunk!"
39 Interlace
41 Paint the town red
42 Netscape or Explorer, e.g.
43 Sorrow
48 Do a cartographer's job over
52 ___ monster (large lizard)
53 Greatest
56 Rival of 41-Across
57 Renfrew refusal
58 "___ not my problem!"
59 Poet's preposition
60 Bon ___ (witticism)

82

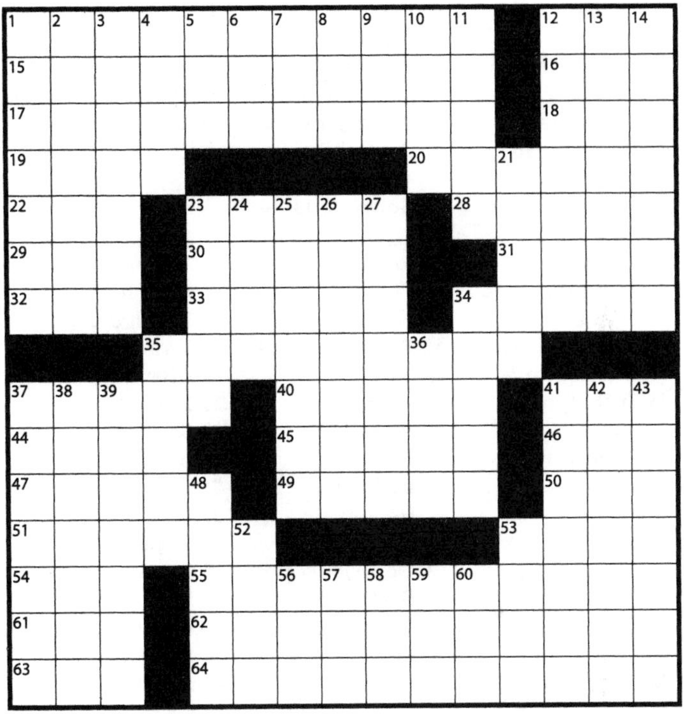
1 2 3 4 5 6 7 8 9 10 11 12 13 14
15 16
17 18
19 20 21
22 23 24 25 26 27 28
29 30 31
32 33 34
35 36
37 38 39 40 41 42 43
44 45 46
47 48 49 50
51 52 53
54 55 56 57 58 59 60
61 62
63 64

60

ACROSS

1 Easily-assembled building
7 Ms. Onassis
13 Big name in coloring
14 Gland near the kidneys
16 Jimmied
17 Bring together again
18 Curve-billed wading birds
19 Strikingly unusual
20 Dove's sound
21 Cooking vessel
24 Savings acct. accrual
25 Hawaiian seaport
27 Roof support
29 Roman censor
30 Richard Burton's ex
33 Neglected items
34 Choice words
40 Mentally healthy
41 Singer Lenya
42 Champagne glass part
43 Oink source
44 Puncture sound
45 "Music for Airports" composer Brian
46 Bolted together?
50 ___ de corps
53 Pitman
55 Placate
56 Novice
57 Rough shelters
58 Scornful expressions
59 Abate

DOWN

1 Heat in advance
2 Pasta cases
3 Good lookers?
4 Golfer's cry
5 Bar brews
6 Evil
7 Preserve
8 "Zip-___-doo-dah!"
9 Pivotal point
10 Bingo's cousin
11 First
12 Destroy by erosion
13 Trite phrase
15 College speaker
21 Fast tempos
22 Commencements
23 Tie-dye garments, often
26 ___ layer (atmosphere part)
27 Government note, for short
28 Peach center
29 Unwanted growths
31 Doctors' gp.
32 Santa ___ winds
34 View
35 Jack-tars
36 Luanda native
37 Repeat
38 Meat from 49-Down
39 Overacts
47 Ballet movement
48 German article
49 Buck or doe
50 Saber relative
51 Health resorts
52 Female swans
54 Small home?
55 Wholly

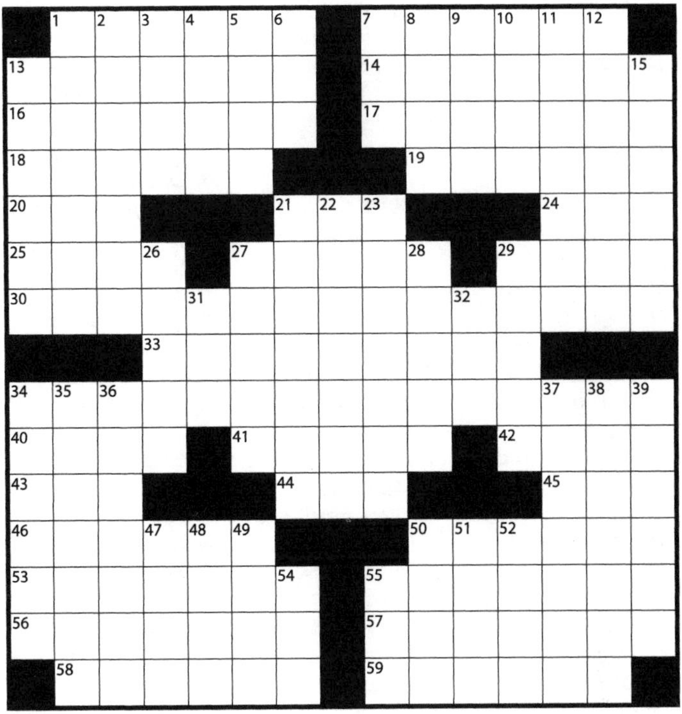

61

ACROSS
1 Sermon
16 E.M. Forster classic
17 Said again
18 Asner and Begley
19 Deity
20 Arrange
21 Perch eggs
22 Chess pieces
23 Three in Italy
25 Arafat's successor
28 Four o'clock drink
31 ___ time (at the appropriate juncture)
35 Diving bird
36 Links
38 Idlers
40 Moon walkers
41 Fare-___-well
42 Old anesthetic
43 Rush
44 Dental ___ (tooth cleaner)
45 Piano support
47 Rap's Dr. ___
48 Muppet eagle
51 Spider's creation
53 Woolly mother
54 Waiter's reward
57 Hand signal, of a sort
61 Chief law officer
62 Obsession

DOWN
1 Decrease gradually, with "down"
2 Imitated
3 Ninnies
4 Mao ___-tung
5 Indians and oranges
6 Boca ___
7 Matured
8 Gave guidance
9 Surmounting
10 Ring-shaped snack
11 Actress Marlene
12 ER workers: Abbr.
13 Kassel's river
14 Farm tower
15 Strongbox
22 Driving spindle
24 Authorize
25 Pond plants
26 Promote
27 Kiosk
28 Synagogue scroll
29 Boredom
30 Make ___ of (jot down)
32 Hawaiian singer
33 Exhorts
34 Double curves
36 Pen pal?
37 French connections
39 Give an early alert
44 City in south-central California
46 "I can't ___ satisfaction ..."
47 Nerd
48 Volvo rival
49 Poker stake
50 Speck
52 Existed
53 Dairy dozen
54 Rotate
55 "Dies ___"
56 Skin
58 Me, to Miss Piggy
59 Henna, for one
60 Gymnast's perfect score

62

ACROSS
1 Lower in value
7 Shrubby tracts
13 Yields to pressure
14 Fernlike plant
15 Authoritative
16 Sham
17 Criminal helper
18 Explosive letters
19 Sense of self
20 Types
21 Finder's cry
22 Biblical garden
23 Mr. ___ (Clue suspect)
24 Counted one's calories
26 French 101 infinitive
27 Most white
29 Old World deer
30 Hate
31 "___ father ..."
34 Ravi Shankar, for one
36 NASDAQ alternative
37 Camera settings
38 Arrives
39 Pitchers
42 "Can ___ honest with you?"

43 Mogadishu native
44 Supped
45 Hydrocarbon ending
46 Work stoppages
47 Unproductive
49 Least elaborate
50 Noisy quarrel
51 Club newcomers
52 Goes in
53 Twilled fabrics

DOWN
1 Comedienne Ellen
2 Shade source
3 Thumped
4 Chips in chips
5 Bustle
6 PC "Help!" key
7 Mesmerizing pro
8 Bridge seat
9 "We ___ not amused"
10 Aligned
11 "___ Podge Lodge" (kids' TV show of the past)
12 Faint
13 Baseball's Alomar

15 Swordlike weapon
18 Rodin masterpiece
21 Fuel line
22 Both Begleys
24 Undress
25 A really big shoe
27 Substantial quality
28 Mattel employees
30 Rehab symptoms, for short
32 Good-for-nothing
33 Withstand
35 Contingencies
36 Political candidate
38 Hollowing out, as an apple
39 "Family Secrets" author Rona
40 Complete reversal of direction
41 Gain access to
43 Flight part
45 Winged
46 ___ gin fizz
48 Put frosting on
49 Nightwear, briefly

63

ACROSS
1 Ivan and Peter, e.g.
6 Glancing blow
15 Tag
16 Trapped
17 Enlighten
18 Terrestrial turtles
19 "The Thinker" sculptor
20 Biblical preposition
21 Put the pedal to the metal
22 Ms. Castle
23 Footlike feature
24 GOP rival group member
25 Stroke lightly
27 Without delay
30 Nautical phenomenon
34 Swedish car manufacturer
38 Spring ___ (let water in)
39 Mediocre
40 ___ light (tanning rays)
43 Will contents
44 Consider
49 Alias
50 Metered vehicle
53 Fervency

54 Op-Ed, for one
56 "___-High City" (Denver's nickname)
57 Variety show
58 Removable furniture protector
60 Paces
61 Using a sifter
62 Beasts of burden
63 Fibbed
64 Run-down

DOWN
1 Churchman
2 Actress Pia
3 Tolerant one
4 Process, as crude oil
5 Foxy quality
6 Pay attention
7 Hole ___ (golfer's dream)
8 Pub game
9 Prefix with plasm
10 Actor Jack of "Barney Miller"
11 Tax deduction
12 Chronic sleeplessness
13 Pressure source, maybe
14 Gaelic language

24 No and Kildare: Abbr.
26 Barrel part
27 Bluffer's game
28 Lateral lead-in
29 Not 'neath
31 Inventor Whitney
32 Cancer follower
33 ___ de mer (seasickness)
34 Go a-courting?
35 Gore and Pacino
36 "Way to go!"
37 Auto stopper
41 ___ distance (afar)
42 Crowd-dispersing weapon
45 Lubricate
46 Counsel
47 Defeated decisively
48 Well-attired
50 Polite
51 Coeur d'___, Idaho
52 Arctic blocks, briefly
54 "Hey you!"
55 Lowest female singing voice
56 "___ Lisa"
59 Resident: Abbr.

64

ACROSS

1 ___ in on (profits from)
7 Mealtime prayers
13 Burros
14 Drinks made with champagne and orange juice
16 Visibly upset
17 Agitates
18 Gracefully thin
19 Dead Sea Scrolls sect member
20 Dollar fractions
21 Pop
24 Dasher's boss
25 "Yes ___?"
26 Military trainee
28 "Happy Birthday" writer, perhaps
29 Flag carriers
32 New ___, Louisiana
33 Natural impulses
41 Word on a biblical wall
42 Peruvian peaks
43 Algerian seaport
44 Muscat native

46 Accelerator
47 Fence crossing
48 Hark back
50 Horse's home
51 Avoiding company
53 Dagger user
54 Citrus drink
55 Word with entry or ignition
56 Make unhappy
57 Magazine extra

DOWN

1 Win over
2 Transmitting aerial
3 Comedian Red
4 Warms
5 Fictional Jane
6 Comic book snake sound
7 Camaros and Corvettes, for short
8 Stravinsky's "The ___ of Spring"
9 Faulty
10 Barbary pirate

11 Nitty-gritty
12 Amble
13 Dance clubs
15 Pop singer Britney
21 Favorite
22 Postscripts
23 Adulterates
26 Actress Gugino
27 Jamboree structures
30 ___ good deed (help out)
31 "___ was saying ..."
33 Without principles
34 Archenemy
35 Unconscious
36 Threatened
37 Famous
38 Cheat sheet user
39 Most lofty
40 Scornful looks
45 Homer epic
47 Remains
49 Fill the hold
50 British carbine
52 Actor Cariou
53 Take to the slopes

ACROSS

1 Shakes up
5 Fixed-price restaurant offering
15 Take flight
16 Exposed to x-rays
17 Norse king
18 Neil Simon movie of 1971
19 Plant tissue
21 Sweet ending?
22 Jimmy ___ (Superman's friend)
23 Snooze
25 ABC rival
26 Garden tool
29 Reno's place: Abbr.
31 Runner Sebastian
32 Adage
35 International understanding
39 Fail to complete
40 Mother's instinct
41 Ave. crossers
42 Like Abner
43 ___ Remo
44 Spelling contest
45 Hyundai partner
46 ___-fi
48 U.S. painter John ___ (1871–1951)

51 Reverence
54 China's Chou ___
58 Disciplinary
61 Singer Vikki
62 Happening now and then
63 Nepal's location
64 "Not allowed!"
65 Basketball's O'Neal, to fans

DOWN

1 "Back to the Future" star Michael ___
2 Friendly nation
3 Genuine
4 Deadly sins number
5 Gratuity
6 Mr. Guthrie
7 Bikini tops
8 Waste time
9 Author LeShan
10 Failure to follow orders
11 Transports by truck
12 Big name in elevators
13 Head, to Henri
14 Early garden
20 Courteous quality

24 Porky Pig's girlfriend
25 Eye pieces
26 Positions of leadership
27 ___ a time (singly)
28 Les ___-Unis
30 Like some sins
31 Hairdos
32 Indian term of respect
33 Coeur d'___, Idaho
34 V-shaped block
36 Night before
37 Toronto Argonauts' org.
38 Wight or Man: Abbr.
45 Gold measure
47 Quechuans
48 Renfrew resident
49 Ness or Lomond
50 Killer whale
51 Like ___ of bricks
52 Sot
53 "Streets of Gold" author Hunter
55 Whip
56 Opera highlight
57 Bagdad's land
59 Hush-hush org.
60 "Turn to Stone" group, for short

1	2	3	4		5	6	7	8	9	10	11	12	13	14
15					16									
17					18									
19				20		21				22				
			23		24				25					
26	27	28		29		30		31				32	33	34
35			36				37				38			
39														
40														
41				42				43				44		
			45							46		47		
48	49	50				51	52	53		54		55	56	57
58					59				60		61			
62											63			
64											65			

66

ACROSS

1 Jump-start
6 Fireplace residue
9 Craze
14 Moon-related
15 Piquant quality
17 Expiate
18 Church musicians
19 Italian noble
20 Indian statesman Jawaharlal ___
21 Heavy weight
22 Leg joint
23 Actor Zimbalist Jr.
25 Kettle and Joad
26 With it, once
29 Word-for-word
33 Supermodel Carol
34 Shortsightedness
36 "___ Only Just Begun"
37 Bravo or Grande
38 What sailors stand on?
40 Camera movement
41 "___ a man with ..."
43 Game player, at times
44 Laurel-Hardy go-between

45 Wormwood-flavored liqueur
47 Draft org.
48 Game units: Abbr.
49 Chick of jazz
51 Nintendo rival
52 French friend
55 Spokes
57 Sacred writings of Islam
58 Montreal hockey team
60 Blazing
61 Having a conversation with
62 Actress Blair
63 Sir ___ Newton
64 Tonic's partner
65 Avid

DOWN

1 Paddy wagon
2 Vulnerable
3 Alert
4 "À votre ___!" (French toast)
5 Oak or elm
6 "___ of the Circus" (John Irving novel)
7 Toot
8 Ambitious people
9 Stately court dance

10 Singer DiFranco
11 Secluded retreat
12 Words of comparison
13 Org.
16 Railcars
24 Feline sound
26 "___ Pinafore"
27 Vision problem
28 Breakfast choice
30 Interior decorator's activity, at times
31 Radically original
32 Listens
35 Gaza gp.
39 Some high schoolers: Abbr.
42 ___-tac-toe
46 ___ combined (skiing event)
50 "___ a stinker?" (Bugs Bunny line)
51 Bulgaria's capital
52 Play opener
53 Goats' cries
54 "To Live and Die ___" (1985 movie)
56 "Time ___ My Side"
57 Hardy cabbage
59 Alias letters

ACROSS

1 Famous outlaw from Centerville
11 Agitate
15 Thrill
16 Best or Ferber
17 Ready to entertain new ideas
18 Comedian Caesar et al.
19 11th U.S. president
20 Grave
22 Gallery display
23 Dignitaries, briefly
27 Cut down
28 AAA recommendation
29 Regions
31 Does some light housework
32 "___ Rosenkavalier"
33 Meld
35 Mile divisions: Abbr.
36 Ill-defined
37 Simile center
40 Decide hastily
41 Director's cry
42 Oregon's capital
45 Himalayan horrors

46 I, to Einstein
47 Cries on camera
49 Mob leaders
50 650, to Ovid
51 Made up one's mind
53 French cheese
54 Banned apple spray
55 Eatery
60 World's longest river
61 "Hard to Swallow" rapper
62 Lip
63 Escapes, of a sort

DOWN

1 Peril
2 Sold abroad
3 Protective structures
4 Kitchen fixture
5 Shade tree
6 ___ alai
7 Prince Valiant's son
8 Nuts
9 Vous ___ (you are, in Montreal)
10 Passover meal
11 Remainder
12 Abominable

13 Place formally in office
14 Scottish maidens
21 Blood group?
23 Cleaned, as a carpet
24 Does pressing work?
25 "Neato!"
26 Set out briskly
30 Taken care of
34 Glossy fabric
37 Corrosive precipitation
38 Concise
39 Olympic Games competitors
40 Collects a pension
42 Family cars
43 Aviation pioneer Earhart
44 Residents
48 Wait tables
52 "Let's Make a ___"
53 Highland hillside
56 Cat or cone prefix
57 Iceberg apex
58 Maugham's "Cakes and ___"
59 Danube city

1	2	3	4	5	6	7	8	9	10		11	12	13	14
15											16			
17											18			
19								20		21				
22				23	24	25	26		27					
28				29				30		31				
32				33				34						
35				36								37	38	39
			40									41		
42	43	44				45						46		
47					48		49					50		
51						52					53			
54					55		56	57	58	59				
60					61									
62					63									

ACROSS

1 London taverns
5 24-hr. banking convenience
8 Dodge models
13 Walking ___ (elated)
15 TV's "___ Na Na"
16 Cote call
17 Prefix with colored
18 For each
19 Repeat sign, in music
20 Ambient music producer Brian
21 Monks
24 Type of pudding
25 Yang's companion
26 More like pitch
28 Conducted
29 Thompson or Samms
31 Different: Prefix
32 "No seats left" sign
33 Extended journeys
35 Munich miss
37 Conjecture
38 Astronaut Grissom
39 "I ___ respect!"

40 Avoidance
42 Consumed
43 Educational inst.
44 Loose paper holder
47 Arctic ice mass
48 Solver's shout
49 Zambian's neighbor
51 Sounds of uncertainty
52 Debtors' chits
54 Senior years
55 Pin cushion?
56 Cotton thread
58 Rep.
59 Pro with a pad
61 Indian, e.g.
62 Name tag?
63 Slight shade
64 Oscar de la ___
65 AMA members
66 French holy women: Abbr.

DOWN

1 Olive Oyl's beau
2 Undisputed pick
3 "The Adventures of ___" (1983 Terry Gilliam movie)
4 Look after junior
5 Have ambitions

6 "Oliver Twist" baddie
7 Priests at weddings, e.g.
8 Dan Rather's network
9 Cries at the bullfight
10 Court award
11 Seasonal citrus fruit
12 Offended, in a way
14 Falling out
22 Pep rally cry
23 Antitoxins
27 Baton ___, Louisiana
30 St. Louis landmark
34 Queen of ___ (Biblical monarch)
36 Page
38 Organized crime
41 Drunkard
45 Tickles pink
46 Poor newspaper
50 Stork's structure
53 Blind part
57 Bambi's aunt
60 "___ the season ..."

ACROSS

1 Conductor Mehta
6 They: French
9 Purplish shade
13 Clear a tape
14 "___ again!"
15 Stags
17 Useful quality
18 Latvia, once: Abbr.
19 Ursa Major neighbor
20 Pear-shaped instrument
21 Takes illegally
23 Shamus
24 Corrida cheer
25 Apt
26 Start of many plays
27 "There!"
29 Ladder parts
30 Actress Perlman of "Cheers"
31 Love story, essentially
34 "Enigma Variations" composer
37 Superlative suffix
38 Whits
39 Weapons of mass destruction
42 Sugar plant
43 Ogle
44 Cosmonaut Gagarin
48 Assocs.
49 Bargain events
50 Scarlet
51 Double helix letters
52 Sums
53 Window shopper's purchase?
54 Duck valued for its down
56 One ___ million
57 Cabal
58 Supercilious
59 Halloween mo.
60 Bay window
61 African antelopes
62 Society page word
63 Rips

DOWN

1 Fanatic
2 Actress Andress
3 Tended, as a turkey
4 "That's logical!"
5 Tennis barrier
6 Dashboard display
7 Fall from a tightrope
8 "I know it's hard to believe ..."
9 Profs, usually
10 Egypt and Syria, once: Abbr.
11 Scrooge's clerk
12 And so on
16 Church parties
21 Agile
22 "___ we forget"
26 Fleet
28 Lets up
32 Former Bruin
33 Kinsman
34 Puts into cipher
35 Memorizing
36 Kipling hero
40 ___ buco (meat dish)
41 Disorderliness
45 Astronomy muse
46 Tenant
47 Paragons
52 "___ bien!"
53 Undiluted
55 End of some web addresses
57 ___ down (make a note of)

70

ACROSS
1 Has an in-tents experience?
6 Astrologer's concern
15 Flashy '60s painting style
16 In a burdensome manner
17 Vigor
18 Dealer's hangout
19 The Goodyear ___
20 Hail unit
21 Baby sitter?
22 Nearly
24 Long-tailed rodent
25 Thin wood strip
26 ___ man (unanimously)
27 Des Moines resident
29 Cloys
30 Camera setting
31 Did intelligence work
32 Eucharist plate
33 Thyroid, e.g.
34 Expectant dad, maybe
35 Saw logs
36 Cat, at times
37 Two-door car

38 300 to 3,000 megahertz on the TV dial
41 "___ it a pity?"
42 Mouth, informally
43 Ogler
45 French connections
46 Iraq's second-largest city
48 "Who's there?" response
49 Dry run
51 Excite
52 Seventh heaven
53 New York's ___ Island
54 Fancy coffees
55 Incline

DOWN
1 Fight
2 Moon mission name
3 Nissan model
4 First-class
5 Wicked Cinderella relative
6 Chief
7 Caught, as a mouse
8 Let borrow again

9 Stoke-on-___, England
10 Flexible tube
11 Big ___, California
12 Quarantined
13 Was smug
14 Woodland deities
23 Bellhop, at times
25 Singer Cleo
28 Took the title
29 Flat-changers' needs
30 Gemstone surface
31 Splashes
32 Hocker's place
33 Wildebeest
34 Soft shades
35 Voice at the opera
36 Penetrate
37 Black currant brandy
38 Actress Andress
39 Surrounds
40 Most autonomous
42 Tall tales
44 Coral reef
46 Commanded
47 Pub pours
50 Asia's neighbor: Abbr.

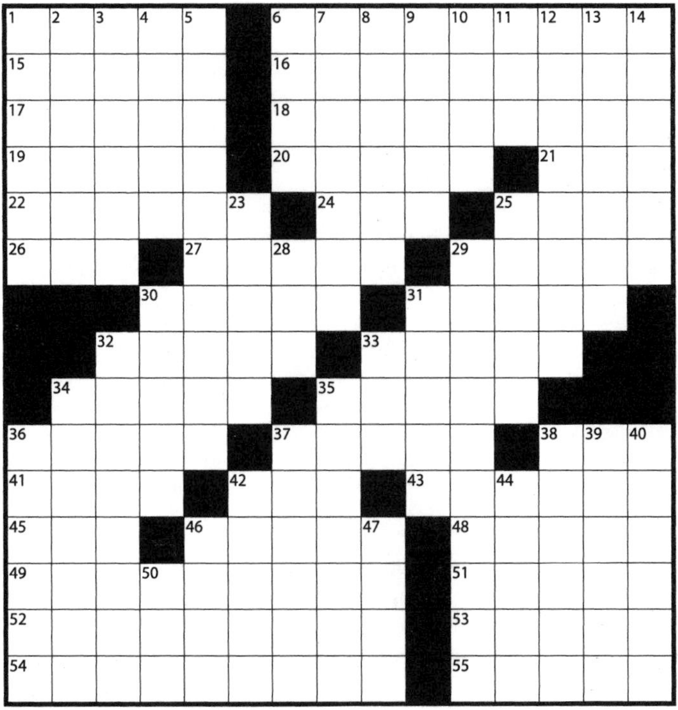

71

ACROSS

1 Frosty, for one
8 It's all talk
15 Patio
16 Toward the source of a stream
17 Passed on, as a message
18 Recent maternity ward arrival
19 Make fit
20 Bridge positions
21 "No, please ... let me!"
24 Yellow-flowered herbs
26 Senator Kennedy
27 "For sure!" in France
29 Flight formation
30 Sign at a sold-out show
31 As a group
32 Serpentine curve
33 Lance competition
34 Slippery ___
37 Walks unsteadily
39 Bach's "Toccata and Fugue ___ minor"
42 Queen or drone
43 Be a precursor of
44 Fannie ___
45 "Nonsense!"
47 On a voyage
49 Clan
50 Grandparent, at times
51 Guts
54 Raise
56 Fate
57 Circular award
58 Lou Grant portrayer
59 Principal dishes

DOWN

1 Narrow channels
2 More impoverished
3 Central Florida city
4 Prepares birthday presents
5 Spring period
6 King beater
7 Homer Simpson's neighbor
8 Shooter
9 Copycat
10 Chocolate treat
11 Parking tickets, e.g.
12 Dodging
13 Small sofas
14 Head locks?
22 "Do You Know the Way to ___"
23 Hutton or Bottoms
24 Coin flippers
25 Vienna's land
28 Fry
34 Receding ocean motion
35 Knowledgeable
36 Singer Etheridge
37 Paying attention
38 Most derogatory
39 Copy
40 "No, No, ___"
41 Thermometer markings
46 Sad notices, for short
48 Devotee
52 Vane dir.
53 Neighbor of Isr.
54 Before, in poesy
55 Actor Chaney

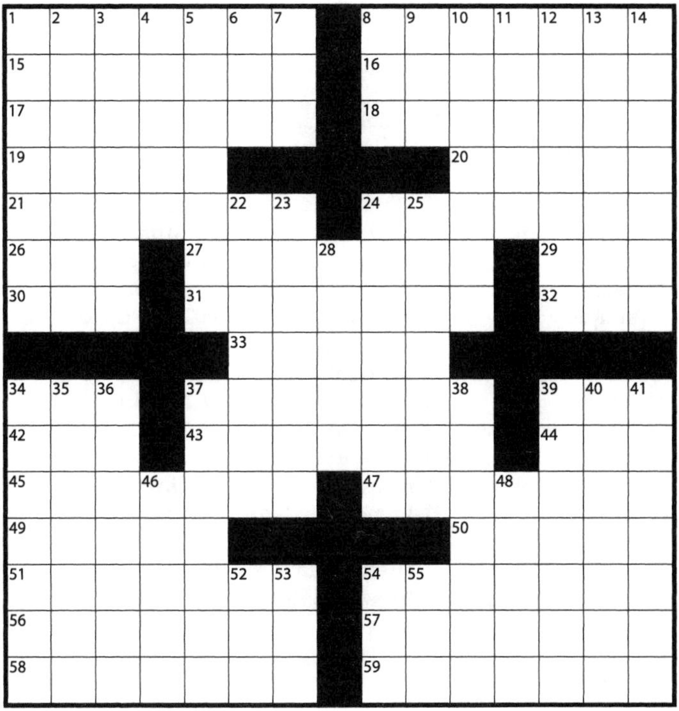
1 2 3 4 5 6 7 8 9 10 11 12 13 14
15 16
17 18
19 20
21 22 23 24 25
26 27 28 29
30 31 32
33
34 35 36 37 38 39 40 41
42 43 44
45 46 47 48
49 50
51 52 53 54 55
56 57
58 59

72

ACROSS
1 Represses
8 Freight train part
15 Not used, as money
16 Egg-shaped wind instrument
17 Hemisphere divider
18 Laundry worker, at times
19 Fontanne's partner
20 Located
22 On ___ with (as good as)
23 Mineral deposit
24 Caboodle's companion
25 Lauda of Grand Prix fame
26 Seine summers
27 Lilies with edible roots
29 Joyride
30 ___ Spiegel
31 Mold anew
33 One of Canada's official languages: Abbr.
34 Dabble in
35 Popular engine additive

38 Dalai Lama, for one
39 U-turn from NNE
42 Biblical ointment
44 More reasonable
45 Costa ___
46 Mayberry moppet
47 Author Deighton
48 Plenty
49 Skid row resident
50 Small pies
52 Brusque
53 Make a note of
55 Hoosier State
57 Immensely large
58 Magnetic field strength unit
59 Heavy artillery fire
60 Birds, in the spring

DOWN
1 Subdued
2 Citation ender
3 Tear ___ (rip into pieces)
4 Floods
5 Irate, with "up"
6 Son of Seth

7 Reaches an equilibrium
8 Fall in
9 Future officer's sch.
10 Prohibition
11 Cathedral instruments
12 Lubricant line
13 Creep past the doorman
14 Lobe decoration
21 Wrench user, at times
27 Big rigs
28 Long stabbing weapon
31 Three before U
32 East ender
35 Cover-up
36 Pearl ___ (cassava)
37 Laser or inkjet
39 Establish
40 Contemptuous type
41 Classified items
43 Himalayan cedar
45 Prejudiced person
50 Small branch
51 Snicker-___
54 Stop ___ dime
56 Surgeons: Abbr.

73

ACROSS
1 Narrow escapes
12 Henry James novel of 1882
14 "Most curious!"
16 Battery terminals
17 Wigwam
18 Crescent-shaped figures
19 Roam, with "about"
22 Wish
23 "___ Brockovich"
24 Followers of epsilons
26 Rub the wrong way
27 Dry, as wine
28 Puts an incorrect label on
30 100-year periods
31 Conductor Arturo
32 Wooden pin
35 Actor Affleck
36 Aerodynamic
37 Digestive juice
38 Talk pompously
40 NFL scores
41 Isinglasses
42 Family member

44 "Rats!"
45 Lawn mower's power, often
49 Go hoarse
50 Kung fu et al.

DOWN
1 Persistent, as a problem
2 Western Netherlands city
3 Off-Broadway awards
4 "___ and Lovers"
5 D.C. clock setting
6 Sault ___ Marie
7 Not vert.
8 Work without ___ (take chances)
9 Clamped
10 Diners
11 Hidden sharpshooters
12 Term of office
13 Word with preview or thief
14 Glens
15 Precious stone

19 Psychological pattern
20 Brought into harmony
21 Milk farms
24 Galvanizing metals
25 Reek
28 Month, in Mexico
29 Hawaiian garland
30 Italian noblewoman
31 Oolong-serving place
32 Outdoor meals
33 Stritch or May
34 "Beau ___"
35 Noisy fight
37 Actress Nilsson
38 Choose
39 Go in
41 Lord's house
43 Horse pace
44 Hindu god
46 "From now ___ am in charge!"
47 Mauna ___
48 Course for recent immigrants: Abbr.

74

ACROSS

1 Star-shaped character
9 Insect stage
14 Sign, as a contract
15 Wrote down
16 Motorist's guide
17 Mix
18 Assam export
19 Light gas
20 Comes up
21 Most distant
23 Warship groups
24 Invest
25 Cheering crowds, e.g.
27 Bull or ram
28 Push out
29 U-turn from NNW
30 Lions, at times
31 Sound of contempt
34 Crash together
35 West Nevada city
36 Indian bean
37 Does a pre-laundry chore
38 Juntas

39 Achieves one's goal
41 Misprints
42 Salary
43 Glob or mod ending
44 Backward-looking
45 It's black on the pool table
47 Guide
48 Phone number parts
49 Easily irritated
50 Kate Bush album of 1993, with "The"

DOWN

1 Insect feelers
2 Span
3 Links prop
4 Once, once
5 Religious ceremonies
6 Stored away unused
7 Mr. Getz
8 Keystone lawman
9 Engenders
10 Tartuffe's creator
11 '40s bomb trials

12 Chromosome parts
13 Chances
14 Regards highly
20 Entice
22 Bar owner on "The Simpsons"
23 Burnt, in a way
26 Anchor position
28 "N-i-c-e!"
30 Relating to circular motion
31 Win over by argument
32 Greater or Lesser West Indies island group
33 Inns
34 Nightclub
35 Eel eggs
36 Menus
37 Comedy routine
38 Canea's island
40 Turkish titles
41 It may come before a while
42 Telegram
45 One of Dumbo's "wings"
46 "What a rotten performance!"

75

ACROSS

1 Confusing procedure
10 Highway approaches
15 Athens attraction
16 Slugger Hank
17 Silent
18 In accordance with the facts
19 Trespasser
21 Oklahoma city
22 Letter carrier's motto word
24 Frozen dessert
25 "Star Wars" creature
29 Fogged up
33 Poet Teasdale
34 Prefix with meter
35 Good tennis server, e.g.
36 Ivan the Terrible, for one
37 Inventor Howe
39 Important periods
41 Priggish person
43 Misfortunes
44 ___ were (so to speak)
45 Aerie
47 Actor Beatty and namesakes

48 Formal requirement
49 Twosome
50 "When I was ___ ..."
52 Shooting one by one
61 Paved the way
63 Calculator forerunner
64 Actress Ryan
65 Robot
66 Black ink entry
67 Red ink entries, maybe

DOWN

1 Hindu princess
2 Double-click PC symbol
3 "True ___" (1969 movie)
4 Musician Allison
5 Mimic
6 "Let's ___!"
7 Butter substitute
8 Speech impediment
9 Necessities
10 Stoolie
11 Swiss river
12 Bodybuilding title
13 SWAT team action
14 TV host Tom

20 Eggs that go to school?
23 Vitamin bottle abbr.
25 Superlative suffix
26 Festive drinkers
27 Citrus drinks
28 Pope John Paul II's real first name
29 Daisy ___ Yokum of the comics
30 Chicago resident
31 Fence crossing
32 Arctic, e.g.
38 Its business was booming
40 Canonized ones: Abbr.
42 Fourposter
45 Literally "and others"
46 Dine
51 Sand hill
53 Hint
54 Singer Eartha
55 Graven image
56 "Nautilus" captain
57 Mardi ___
58 Means of escape
59 Ice mass
60 Marshlands
62 Domesticated animal

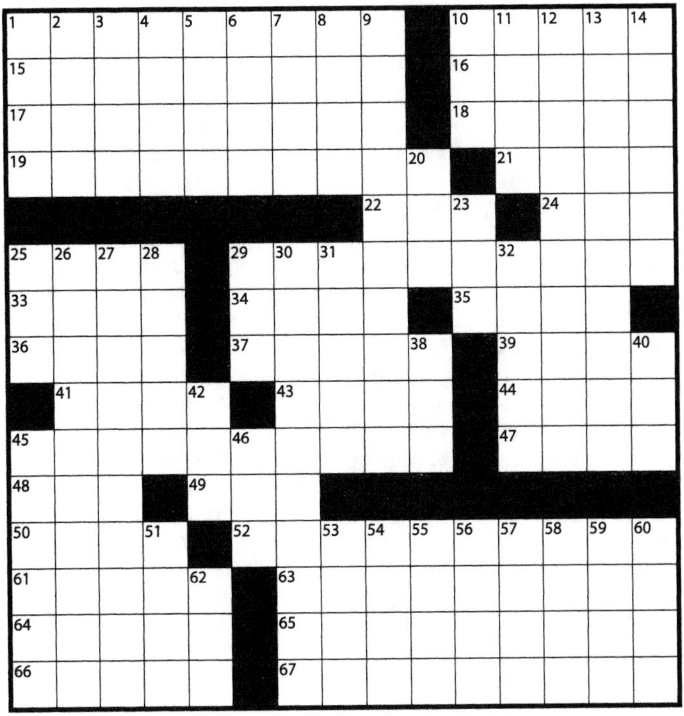

76

ACROSS

1 Banquet attendee
8 "Leda and the Swan" poet
15 Fire up
16 Poor person
17 The Waldorf-___ (NYC hotel)
18 Torpor
19 "Mum's ___!"
20 CFL scores
21 "Kidnapped" author's monogram
22 Previously, previously
23 Cook slowly
25 Hit hard
26 Two-faced Roman god
27 "You picked ___ time to leave me, Lucille ..."
29 At the apex of
30 Strengthening
35 "___ cares!"
36 Drain
37 ___ standstill (motionless)
38 Undivided
39 Upper school
42 Leaning Tower's location

43 Rage
44 Floral feature
45 Stuffs
48 "Casablanca" lady
50 "When I was ___ ..."
51 In the past
52 Alternatives to Macs
53 "Waltzing ___"
56 Beef, e.g.
58 Down for the count
59 Fencer's cry
60 Laundered
61 Edible clam
62 Weird quality

DOWN

1 Italian car company
2 Cover, as a sword
3 P.M. period
4 Decelerates
5 Oracles' cards
6 Kuwaiti VIP
7 Interprets
8 Sign of surrender
9 Data transmission rate
10 ___ Saint Laurent

11 Suffix with election
12 Bone cavities
13 Labors
14 Secret supply
24 Mai ___ (rum drink)
25 Gandhi portrayer Kingsley
26 Peter Benchley shocker
28 Ms. Peeples
30 Roadblock
31 Pad, as furniture
32 Eschew help
33 Throws, as a horseback rider
34 Belfry sound
36 Worthless coin
40 Conditions
41 Tax org.
42 Large-billed seabird
44 Hit lightly
45 Merchandise
46 Broker
47 Viper maker
49 Big name in oil
52 Salon set
54 "___ Lang Syne"
55 Puts two and two together
57 Nanny's bleat

ACROSS

1 "Le Coq ___" (Rimsky-Korsakov opera)
4 Hidden drawback
9 Take ___ down memory lane
14 Actress Sue ___ Langdon
15 Nebraska city
16 Big name in march music
17 Kingston Trio hit
18 In an unfunny manner
20 Interrogative interjections
21 Compass pt.
22 Narc's org.
23 ___ Paulo
24 Recent: Prefix
25 Mend, as a shoe
27 Hostelry
28 Banks and Kovacs
30 Soprano Te Kanawa
32 Cannon or stock follower
33 Cargo
34 Go astray
35 Shiny elements
37 Name
39 Half and half?

40 Mistake
41 Lounges around
42 Salad server
43 Tops
44 Summer abroad
45 Attracted
47 Krispy Kreme products
49 Bon ___ (witty remark)
50 Makes a speech
52 Rim
53 Before, to Byron
54 Charged particle
55 Frequently, in poesy
56 Chemical ending
57 Tabloid's specialty
60 Gumshoe
61 Silly girl
62 Move sideways
63 It's a blast
64 Photographer Adams
65 Sooth follower
66 Spaceship drivers

DOWN

1 Enrico Caruso contemporary
2 Headed for a downfall

3 "Low monthly payments," e.g.
4 Stick
5 Tickles pink
6 Subdues
7 Comedian Margaret
8 Uncompromising one
9 On the Azov
10 Lean-___ (sheds)
11 "Game" played with a gun
12 Australia, e.g.
13 Show up at a funeral
19 Ogle
26 WWII island
29 ___ fixe
31 Suffix with computer
34 Judge's attribute?
36 Persia today
38 Timothy Leary's drug
46 Crucifix
47 Tarnish
48 Stable worker
51 Sycophant
54 Graven image
58 "How could ___ so stupid?"
59 Acapulco aunt

ACROSS
1 On-ramp sign
6 Scrub, as a mission
11 Patty Hearst's kidnappers: Abbr.
14 Tusk material
15 Pride of lions?
16 Peppery
17 Date anew
18 Escapes, as from jail
20 Domains
21 Numero ___
22 "___ were the days ..."
23 Arrive at
24 Day light
25 Peaceful form of civil disobedience
26 Organic compound
27 Medical org.
28 Struck, in a way
29 Two-channel
31 Get ___ (ace the course)
33 Is incorrect
34 14-line poems
37 Botanical bristle
41 ___ Xing (street sign)

42 Consumes completely
47 Separate
49 ABC rival
51 San ___, California
52 Sixth sign of the zodiac
53 "Krazy ___"
54 Pound sounds
55 All the stage is his world
56 Untruth
57 "Green ___" (TV oldie)
58 Belize neighbor
60 Topic
61 Suffix with south
62 Went like the wind
63 Piles
64 ___ Plaines, Illinois
65 Follows orders
66 Seamen

DOWN
1 Desert illusions
2 Himalayan high point
3 Circular cluster of leaves
4 Larger
5 Ugly structures
6 Waylay

7 Big names in big tops
8 Man-to-man
9 Actor Stephen of "The Crying Game"
10 Sound of disapproval
11 Person throwing the dice, in craps
12 Worse
13 Shows up
19 Glisten
30 "Alley ___"
32 Breakfasted
35 Ornamental chain
36 Days of rest
37 Attacked violently
38 Gourmet
39 Plaid patterns
40 Patois
43 Windpipe, in anatomy
44 Dreamlike
45 Messy
46 Have
48 Matador
50 Bed and home followers
59 Mercutio's Queen ___ speech

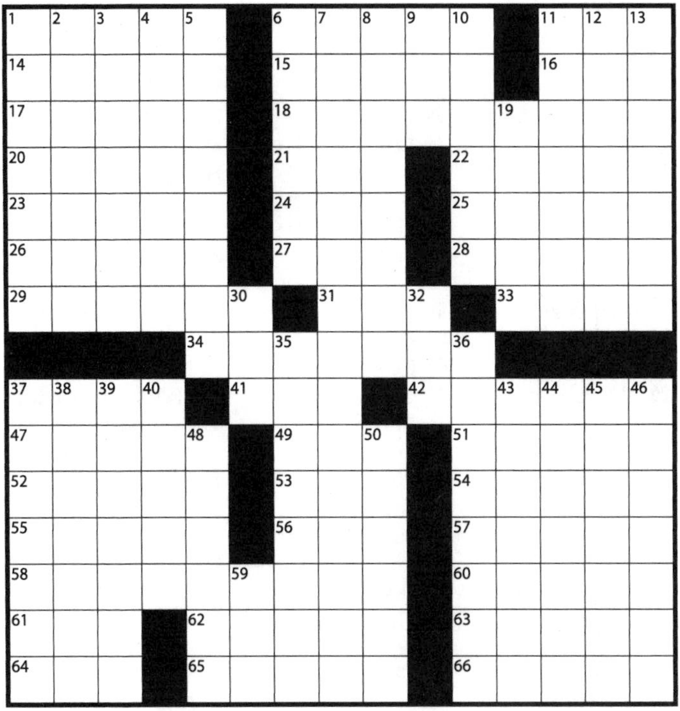

ACROSS
1 Membranes
6 Needlefish
9 Home ___ (catcher's place)
14 Addicts
15 Compass dir.
16 Fit for a king
17 Conductor's wand
18 "Ouch!" relatives
19 Viscounts' superiors
20 "More than ___!" ("Brains too!")
23 Flying horse of Greek myth
24 Tears
28 Black tea variety
29 Tubular pasta
33 ___ Heep
35 Ballerinas
37 Late English princess
38 GI's WWII entertainer
39 Growl
40 Decent chap
42 Headdress for 37-Across
43 Spanish 101 word
44 Bread producer
46 Fraudulent affair
47 Contusions

49 Horse racing's epithet
57 "Boléro" composer
58 Call ___ day (quit)
59 "Take ___!" (usher's request)
60 "Farewell!"
61 Poet's contraction
62 Mouth-watering
63 Date producers
64 Hosp. employees
65 County in England

DOWN
1 Topic: Abbr.
2 Seesaw sitter of tongue twisters
3 Favorites
4 Moderately swift pace
5 "Piece of cake!"
6 English illustrator and novelist (1834–96)
7 Very feeble
8 Relaxes after exertion
9 Victimizes, with "on"
10 Oolong unit
11 Taj Mahal site

12 Powdery mineral
13 "Or ___!"
21 Liveliness
22 Mon. follower
24 Magistrate
25 Zodiac opener
26 Beanstalk baddie
27 Rudolph's boss
29 New Mexico natives
30 Author Asimov
31 ___ cotta
32 Muslim faith
34 "2001" computer
36 Braggart's favorite suffix
41 Spanish river
45 Sports official, for short
47 Grade below A minus
48 Large edible ray
49 Links hazard
50 "If I ___ Hammer"
51 Apt anagram for "vile"
52 Appear
53 "Handsome ___ handsome does"
54 Cape
55 Movable barrier
56 Underworld river

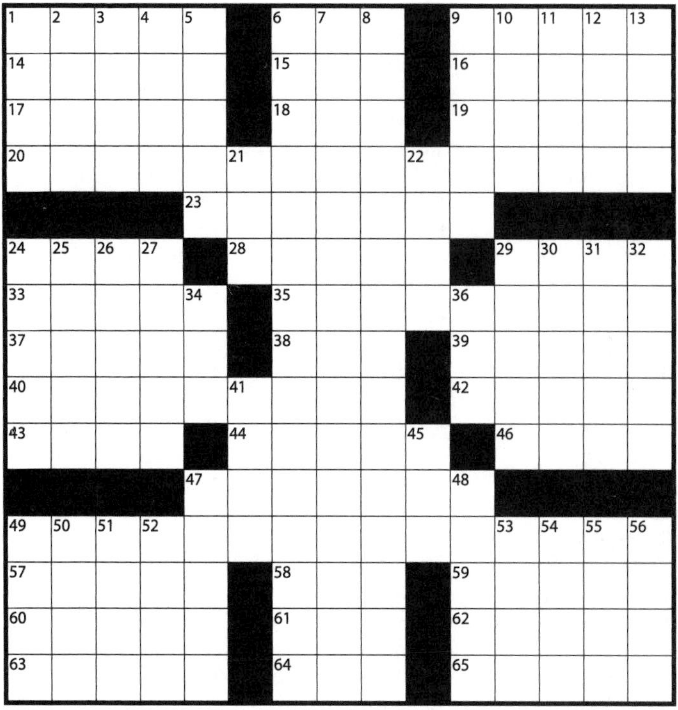

80

ACROSS
1 Moral principles
7 Game similar to horseshoes
13 Like a damp sponge
14 A-bomb ingredient
16 "Teenage Mutant Ninja ___"
17 Acute
18 ___ Tin Tin
19 Newt
20 Mao's middle name?
21 ___ Kan
22 Map within a map
24 Play part
26 Loathsome
27 Cosmetician Lauder
32 "Rule Britannia" composer
33 Knowledgeable testifiers
36 Hindu monarchs
37 Boomeranged
43 Writer Hunter
44 Mama's boy
45 Good buddy
46 Popular Dodge models of yore
48 Pack leader

49 Mr. Onassis, to friends
50 Owns
53 Blood group letters
55 Honolulu garland
56 Ceremonies
58 Jury's finding
60 "The ___ Pimpernel"
61 Affirms
62 Upper classes
63 Meat cuts

DOWN
1 March or September event
2 Arrives
3 Collide with
4 Land in the lake?
5 Professional cook
6 Method: Abbr.
7 Drop out
8 Big vases
9 Author Joyce Carol ___
10 Ending with Ernest
11 Pot menders
12 Actress Benton of "A Boy and His Dog"

13 Discord
15 Riotous fights
23 Periodic table entry
25 Clerical garment
27 Community character
28 Hindu religious teacher
29 Exhausts
30 States: French
31 Savor
34 Cheerleader's chant
35 Attention
37 Coniferous trees
38 Greed
39 Pertaining to a husband and wife
40 Stone pillar
41 Picks
42 Attributes
47 "Thou ___ not ..."
48 Blood line?
51 Aweather's opposite
52 Fast flyers, for short
53 Actress Gardner et al.
54 Second Hebrew letter
57 Spoon-bender Geller
59 Bear's lair

81

ACROSS

1 ___ snag (run into problems)
5 Trailer
15 "A miss ___ good ..."
16 Relating to body structure
17 Clench
18 Office supplies merchants
19 Hearty companion?
20 Performs alone
21 "Done!"
22 Chopped
23 French patron saint
24 Yale attendees
25 Entered uninvited, as a party
30 German article
31 Popular hymn
35 Old Ford models
37 Theater employee
38 Rainy day rarity
39 Big Mac bun topper
41 A-E links
42 Thin plain-weave cotton
43 Saskatchewan native

44 Ice cream server
47 Feels feverish
48 Stretched tight
49 Tea-producing Indian state
54 "___ we forget"
55 Frozen continent
57 Nastase of tennis
58 Objective
59 Splashing sound
60 Drowsy state
61 Towel word

DOWN

1 Raised shoes
2 Hebrew
3 They blow in the traveler's direction
4 Poplar trees
5 Volume
6 Aware of
7 False god
8 "Leave ___ Beaver"
9 Hi's partner in comics
10 Comedian Philips
11 Made allusions about

12 Large water body
13 ___ Gras
14 Lanchester and Maxwell
23 Dictionary offering: Abbr.
25 Vinegar server
26 Martini's partner
27 Feels sore
28 Sport of clay pigeon shooting
29 Multitude
32 "Scent of a Woman" actress Anwar
33 New York's state motto
34 Eludes
36 Undermine
40 Navigator's need
43 Muslim religious leader
44 They may be vital
45 Panama or Suez
46 Eccentric
49 "Julius Caesar" opener
50 Mr. Getz
51 Mare's mate
52 High cards
53 Farmyard sounds
56 Bodybuilder's motion

126

82

ACROSS
1 Load, as cargo
5 Lad's counterpart
9 "___ worse than death"
14 Mata ___
15 Habituated
17 Norse king
18 Lace
19 Sheep shelter
20 Looks after
21 Type of arch
22 Massage
24 Low grade
25 One-armed bandits
26 Pen point
28 Club ___
29 They may flock together
38 Synthesizer relative
39 1986 movie with Tom Hanks and Jackie Gleason
40 Seine sight
41 "You ___ here"
42 Booth
45 Circle section
48 Former Winter Palace residents

52 ___ one's way (travel)
53 Cordwood measure
55 Slide sideways
56 Neon and xenon, e.g.
58 Yorkshire river
59 Urban light
60 Chrysler product of the '80s
61 Alan Ladd title role of 1953
62 Actor Bremner
63 Congers

DOWN
1 Traumatize
2 Eagle's weapon
3 Speak in public
4 Certain family members
5 Endure
6 Yearned
7 Quick bread
8 "Blue ___ Shoes"
9 ABA member
10 "Again!"
11 Monterrey pal
12 Dogma
13 Outer limits?
16 Serpent's sound

23 Purify
25 Harbor city
27 Carrying
28 Place of pilgrimage
29 London's Big ___
30 UN agcy.
31 Collecting a pension: Abbr.
32 Mist
33 Black cuckoo
34 Shark's appendage
35 Bad actor
36 Ambient music pioneer Brian
37 Reagan, to friends
42 Zurich natives
43 Agent's take, often
44 The end of ___
45 Start of a Dickens title
46 Cut anew
47 ___ de menthe
49 Wonderland girl
50 Bucolic
51 Futurists
53 Cpl.'s superior
54 Games network
57 Links device

ACROSS

1 Loses consciousness
10 Supercilious
15 Put between
16 Winkler of "Happy Days"
17 Self-righteous type
18 Change hair color again
19 Tendency
20 Shortens
21 Mad scientist's hangout
22 "A mouse!"
24 Likewise
25 ___ out a living (barely gets by)
27 Graph
30 Have on
31 Additional
33 Gruff
35 Third place finishers
39 Arthur Conan Doyle's "The Red-Headed ___"
40 Fifth canonical hour
41 Elects
42 Emulate Sonya Henie
44 Public lecture

48 WWII U.S. Army gp.
49 Guys
50 Female rabbit
51 Grand instrument?
53 Put aside
59 Annoyed
60 Judicial system goal
61 Pet problem?
62 CIA specialty
63 Car bomb?
64 Became more difficult to climb

DOWN

1 Acne spot
2 Parka
3 Flashing light
4 Actor Penn
5 Author ___ Stanley Gardner
6 Rotate
7 Seep
8 Employs
9 More to the point
10 2001 Dreamworks animated hit
11 Welfare state?
12 Poets, e.g.
13 Unbuttered breakfast food

14 Offensive sights
23 Fuel gas
26 Airs
27 Brie or feta, e.g.
28 ___ and haw
29 Gladiator's milieu
30 Spare tire location?
32 Lao-___ (Chinese philosopher)
34 Bullfight cheer
35 Poison dart propeller
36 Mended
37 Scottish treats
38 Period
43 Uses a dagger on
45 Actor ___ Zmed
46 Parsley relative
47 Toppled, with "over"
49 Exemplar
52 Actress Campbell of "Scream"
54 Cartoonist Thomas
55 Ready for picking
56 Toledo's lake
57 Organ control
58 Sea eagle

84

ACROSS

1 Recipe amt.
4 Barfly
11 Comedian Carrey
14 ___ Miss
15 Electromotive force
16 Actress Merkel
17 Stimpy's chum
18 Cooked eggs, in a way
19 Communication for the hearing-impaired: Abbr.
20 Close
22 Thyme, e.g.
23 Make a sweater
24 Breathing problem
26 Letters on European speedometers
27 Sarcastic
28 Ism
30 Carries
31 Puzzle opener
33 "See if ___!"
34 Go the distance
35 Watch sound
37 Randy of "Independence Day"
40 Retreats stealthily
45 Arm bones
46 Large choral work
47 Uncles' mates

48 Baddie in "The Lord of the Rings"
49 "The ___ Limits"
50 Run away
51 Chris of tennis fame
53 Raced
54 Send an image by phone
55 Individualized Internet symbols
57 Fleur-de-___
58 Summer on the Seine
59 Triple time dances
60 Ginger ___ (soda choice)
61 ___ Plaines
62 Trying person
63 "Bill ___, the Science Guy"

DOWN

1 Twister
2 Postpone, as a decision
3 Voluntary self-punishment
4 Sets in the living room
5 ___ and aahs
6 Nooses
7 Chevron parts
8 Cause to wither
9 Type of arch

10 Danson of "Cheers"
11 Actress Moore of "Imitation of Life"
12 ___ trading (stock market crime)
13 "The ___ Falcon" (1941 movie)
21 Get even
23 Renders unconscious
25 Pinball palaces
27 ___ one's guns (stand firm)
29 Tax org.
32 Restless from confinement
36 "Never ___ million years!"
37 Drank
38 Howl
39 Building additions
41 Singer Lynn
42 Old World bunting
43 With a passionate fervor
44 Anticipate
48 Facial shapes
51 Gabor and Perón
52 Forest feature
55 Veneration
56 Estonia, once: Abbr.

ACROSS

1 Dancer Duncan
8 Shakespearian poems
15 Dangling decorations
16 ___ cushion (prankster's device)
17 Dominate
18 Drains
19 Sermon ending
20 "Never!"
22 Prefix with girl
23 "Wayne's World" word
24 Average
25 Resistance unit
26 Membership payments
28 The brainy bunch
30 Captain Hook's cohort
31 Walked proudly
33 Hardworking
35 Many
37 Silent movie star ___ Naldi
38 Gulf of Mexico port
42 Thomas Alva ___
46 Champagne bucket
47 Sandwich cookies
49 Neck part
50 Plaudit of a sort
51 Thai language
52 Asian holiday
53 Covers
55 Playwright Oscar
57 Malicious gossip
58 Gourmet
60 Football pass
62 Flies in the tropics
63 Christian recluse
64 Butler, e.g.
65 Edited, as film

DOWN

1 Is about to happen
2 Put in order
3 Aider and ___
4 Headlong plunge
5 Ending with pay or play
6 Part of a harness
7 Tilting
8 Administers an oath to
9 "Gosh!"
10 M-Q links
11 ___ bene
12 Typical example
13 Develops molars
14 Certain bagels
21 "All I ___ for Christmas ..."
27 Type of heat or panel
28 Subway
29 Pisces follower
30 Killed
32 Sawbones
34 JFK listing
36 Most grumpy
38 Shrinking flowers?
39 Overshadow
40 More oboelike
41 Ardor
43 Cutting, as humor
44 Manage
45 Irked
48 Scads
54 John Candy's old show, briefly
55 St. Paul's Cathedral architect
56 Tombstone's Wyatt
57 Half: Prefix
59 Can. neighbor
61 ___ Aviv

86

ACROSS

1 "Howards End" actress
16 Mario Cuomo, for one
17 Almost one fifth
18 Early Nebraskan
19 NYC clock setting
20 River to the Baltic Sea
21 The Platters hit of 1955
25 Flexible strip
29 Washday whitener
34 Weds
38 Suffix with usher
39 Dundee denial
40 "___ jail" (Monopoly square)
41 Put on one's best clothes
46 Military raid
47 Company haters
48 Acclamation
52 "Do, ___, fa ..."
56 151, in old Rome
57 Director Kazan
61 Aspiring officeholder's speech
66 Heart and liver, e.g.
67 Stop misbehaving, after a spanking

DOWN

1 Wine, in Italy
2 Hard ___ (busily working)
3 Prefix with second
4 Gen. Robt. ___
5 Make a lap
6 Manuscript enclosure: Abbr.
7 Slippery as ___
8 Actor Quaid
9 "E," on a gas gauge
10 Actor Billy ___ Williams
11 Terrier's warning
12 Puerto ___
13 Passed easily, as an exam
14 Windmill part
15 ___'acte
21 Light switch positions
22 Meshwork
23 British award: Abbr.
24 Suffix with form
25 Snow day toys
26 Prefix with dollar or chemical
27 Subsequently
28 Literally "that is"
30 ___ Marbles (British Museum treasure)
31 Do penitence

32 Provide food
33 Former presidential candidate ___ Perot
35 Artist Yoko
36 Make lace
37 Prankster's laugh
42 Small drink
43 ___ Aviv
44 Whitney or Wallach
45 "___ if I can help it!"
49 Flip ___ (toss for it)
50 Radius neighbors
51 Gauges
52 Projector part
53 Additional
54 Flat-topped hill
55 Cake decorating specialist
57 Energy units
58 Meadows
59 "Ignorance of the law ___ excuse!"
60 Org.
62 Former C&W cable network
63 "How was ___ know?"
64 U.S. currency, briefly
65 Rap producer Dr. ___

136

87

ACROSS
1 Building bar
6 Coil
11 Skillet
14 Alfred E. Neuman's publication
16 Suffix with elephant
17 Changes
18 Sgt., e.g.
19 Soda servers: Var.
20 Harness part
21 Comprehend
24 First-rate
25 Dawn goddess
26 Becoming outdated
33 "The Waste Land" poet's monogram
34 Some neutron stars
35 Summer, in Montreal
36 Sargasso or Salton
37 Grassland
38 Actress Joanne
39 Enterprise letters
40 Whole number
41 Development site

42 Be a good borrower
44 Comedian Philips
45 X-ray units
46 Hedda's creator
48 "For ___ jolly good ..."
49 Tapioca source
54 Artist Jean ___
55 Go ballistic
59 Hilo garland
60 Pretended
61 Purcell piece
62 Shovel
63 Leavening agent

DOWN
1 "___ father!"
2 Dance, in Dijon
3 Ont. summer clock setting
4 In ___ (untidy)
5 Disney governess
6 "Hell ___ no fury ..."
7 Basso Pinza
8 Jungle king
9 Hotels
10 Crosses out
11 Forest floor covering, maybe
12 Nero's milieu
13 ___ tetra (flashy fish)

15 Opening
20 Mythical bird of prey
21 Leaves bed
22 Start of some four-line poems
23 Simple
24 How the confident may speak
27 Incinerated
28 List of candidates
29 Willow twig
30 Big
31 Spooky-sounding tribe?
32 Early German
43 Actress Lupino
47 Musical Count
48 Circle of light
49 Thunder sound
50 Verdi opera
51 Put the pedal to the metal
52 "___ it!" ("Amen!")
53 Chemical ending
55 Some radios: Abbr.
56 Actress Thompson
57 Hosp. hookups
58 The Tigers, on scoreboards

138

ACROSS
1 Space station energy producer
11 Barnyard bleats
15 Enterprise
16 Type of D.A.
17 Directory assistance info
19 Champion's cry
20 Abbey et al.: Abbr.
21 Prefix with skeleton
22 Scottish negative
23 "___ first you don't ..."
27 Concludes successfully
29 Org.
30 Nobelist Bergson
32 Hayworth and Moreno
33 Grading
35 D.C. insider
36 Delano for Roosevelt and Milhous for Nixon, e.g.
38 Drench
39 Oil-bearing seeds
40 Harbor
42 Lugs
43 Jackson 5 hit
46 Stadiums
48 Monster's loch
49 FDR program
50 Lamb's dad
51 American uncle
53 ___ about (approximately)
54 Amperage
60 Washroom sign
61 Collect
62 ___ precedent
63 Salon offerings

DOWN
1 Peaceful protests
2 Unidirectional
3 Symbols of whiteness
4 Two fives for ___
5 Tombstone inscription
6 Exclamation of disgust
7 From ___ Z (the gamut)
8 Diarist Anaïs
9 Always
10 Imparts
11 Comic book impact sound
12 Fireproof substance
13 Lacking gender
14 Razor sharpeners
18 Mouse manipulator
23 "But ___ no choice!"
24 Resists, with "off"
25 Leg ornament
26 Checks the fit of
28 Obliterates, with "out"
31 Present at birth
33 Age
34 Tennis units
36 Symphony division
37 Military diner
38 Big name in frozen desserts
40 Ladies rooms?
41 American cartoonist Thomas
43 Toughen by heating
44 Charlotte or Emily
45 Menus
47 Skater Hughes
52 Flaky mineral
53 Airport near Paris
55 Union opponents: Abbr.
56 Third-century date
57 Mongrel
58 No-see-___ (tiny insects)
59 Furrow

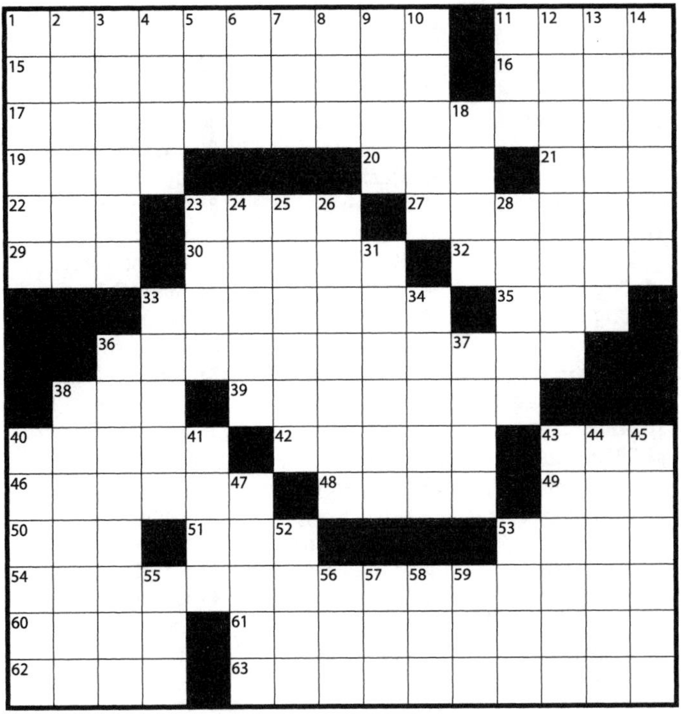

89

ACROSS

1 Hockey disks
6 Interplanetary craft
15 "___ Like It" (Shakespeare play)
16 Friction reducer
17 Summarize briefly
18 City folks
19 City in central France
20 Investigate anew, as a case
21 Pointed weapons
23 UFO pilots, perhaps
24 Newsweek rival
28 "Les ___"
30 Attach, as blame
31 "Like this clue"
36 Nervous ___
37 Warned audibly
39 Roofing tiles
40 Erodes, with "at"
41 Studio stand
42 Ultimate degree
43 "What's ___ for me?"
44 Track circuit
47 Cried loudly
52 Triumphant cry
55 Chicago airport
56 F-16 propulsion
59 Seized
60 Demon ousters
61 Vote
62 Blockhead's attribute
63 Musical symbols

DOWN

1 Roles
2 Deplete
3 Go by bike
4 Australian marsupial
5 Highly paid poser
6 Disparaging remark
7 Blender food
8 Monk's superior
9 Dice game
10 Mozart's "___ kleine Nachtmusik"
11 Scarcely detectable amount
12 Lid
13 Follower of Paul?
14 Mr. Barnum et al.
22 Locations
25 Relative by marriage
26 Dancer Shearer
27 Foe
29 British alphabet ender
30 Brat's weapon
31 Japanese immigrant
32 "Memento" director Christopher
33 Resembling: Prefix
34 Takes off a leash
35 Sault ___ Marie
36 Meshlike
38 Solo of "Star Wars"
44 Connect to a computer network
45 Originate
46 Gasps
48 Ocean heavyweight
49 Huron and Ontario
50 Upright
51 Fender blemishes
53 Formerly
54 Pianist Myra
56 Jethro's uncle on TV
57 Devon river
58 Long or short weight

90

ACROSS

1 Get comfortable, in a way
16 Harris/Anderson western of 1970
17 Temporary hospital
18 Committee pro ___
19 Oft-picked item
20 Terminate
21 Minded junior
23 Bikini atoll event
25 Singletons
26 Come-___ (enticements)
28 Clue
30 It may keep sleepers up
34 In ___ (overdue, as a payment)
37 Ideal places
38 More damp
39 Installs machinery
40 Pale colors
41 Bobbin
42 "___ Eagle has landed!"
43 Swimmer's exercise
45 Ridicules
49 Hit lightly
52 Eggs, in anatomy
53 "___ little teapot ..."
54 Clergyman's deg.
56 Simple surgical procedures
63 Joined up
64 Very limber

DOWN

1 27th U.S. president
2 French girlfriends
3 Fate
4 Pulver's rank: Abbr.
5 Halloween mo.
6 Airport overseer: Abbr.
7 Michigan town
8 Classic song
9 Robins' retreats
10 Apr. clock setting in NYC
11 Na Na lead-in
12 Camp bed
13 Determine one's position
14 How two hearts may beat
15 Keeps watch on
22 Causes to fall
23 Physical attack
24 Carburetor parts
25 Old dance
27 Librarian's bane
29 Type of stew or coffee
30 Nevertheless
31 Ike's WWII command
32 Portal part
33 Recipe abbreviation
34 Current unit
35 Prot. or Cath., e.g.
36 Grads-to-be: Abbr.
43 "___ luck!"
44 Swears
46 "The Importance of Being Earnest" author
47 "... ___ man with seven ..."
48 RPM gauges
50 ___ acids (dietary necessities)
51 Arduous journeys
55 In ___ (existing)
57 Road sign
58 UN agcy.
59 Guitarist Paul
60 It's in the bag
61 Assn.
62 "Little Red Book" author

144

91

ACROSS
1 Painter Pablo
8 Fragrant shrub
15 Sluggishness
16 Wears away
17 Brown-speckled bird
18 Nasty guys
19 Runners, of a sort
20 Mr. Clampett
21 Word before fountain or jerk
22 Hole ___ (golfer's dream)
23 Possesses
24 Itsy-___
25 Philosopher Descartes
26 Prepare leather
27 Pen name of Dickens
28 Superlative suffix
29 About eight kilometers
32 Medium-value playing card
35 They're three digits long
36 Liquid dosage units: Abbr.
38 "___ bodkins!"
39 Fall asleep, with "off"
40 Pitcher Saberhagen

41 Barcelona bulls
44 Sts.
45 Actress Davis
46 Egg, to Caesar
47 Ewe said it
48 Stiff straw hat
49 Inhabitant
51 Ardent nationalist
52 Speaking in a monotone
53 Surpassed
54 ___ Kiang (Asia's longest river)
55 Mary Tyler Moore's boss on TV

DOWN
1 Ant
2 Pitch-black quality
3 Export of Sri Lanka
4 Francis or Dahl
5 Rubberneck
6 Letter opener
7 Furniture wood
8 Author ___ Joyce
9 All tucked in
10 Madrid Mrs.
11 Large, in a way
12 Fool

13 Requires
14 Literary composition
20 "Barbarella" actress
23 Mayhem
24 Gauchos' ropes
26 Turner and Louise
27 Two-footed animal
29 Nourishes
30 PC operating system
31 Earwax, e.g.
33 Roaring, as an engine
34 Act opener
37 Track meet official
40 Facial growths
41 Hot ___ (warm drink)
42 ___ barrel (stuck)
43 Continue uninterrupted
44 Kitchen fixture
45 "Ya ___ love it!"
47 Mercedes-___
48 Data transmission unit
50 Teenage spot?
51 Author Edgar Allan ___

146

ACROSS

1 Path blockers
10 Eject
14 Fancy cabins on a ship
15 Large moth
16 NBC's peacock preceded them
17 Help for the impoverished
18 "___ bells!"
19 Crosses out
20 Cove
21 Casting requirement?
23 Slow to learn
24 Rock's ___ Speedwagon
26 Nervous
30 Professor's deg.
31 In the near future
33 Illinois airport
34 Cook book?
35 Speechless
36 Origami medium
37 From the top
38 "Forever ___ Day" (1943 movie)
39 Amphitheater
40 Musical Horne
41 ___ Victor
42 Cut in three
44 Porker's place
45 "Arabian Nights" sailor

47 Makes lace
49 Crème de ___
50 Clay, today
53 ___ Island Red
56 Elevator pioneer
57 Personal automobile
59 Closely confined, with "up"
60 Slippery peel
61 "The ___ of Night"
62 Unfeeling quality

DOWN

1 Early Nebraskan
2 Astaire's specialty
3 Mink scarf
4 Less wordy
5 Electrical discharge
6 Wheedle
7 Misplace
8 Ambulance attendants: Abbr.
9 Comic book puncture sound
10 Incline
11 Prepare to make a greater effort
12 Tangling
13 Became skin and bone

14 Educational inst.
20 "Where would ___ without you?"
22 Large black-spotted cat
23 Ham it up
24 Blip producer
25 Articulated
27 Lamb Chop's creator ___ Lewis
28 Cassettes
29 Goodnight girl
32 Hoopster's org.
34 Nev. neighbor
42 "The ___ of Pooh" (Benjamin Hoff book)
43 Plaid
46 Keep moist, as a turkey
48 "One of ___ days ..."
50 What the suspicious may smell
51 Floor covering, for short
52 ___ the Terrible
54 Pulpit
55 North or south follower
57 "Nova" network
58 "Traci, spelled with ___"

93

ACROSS

1 Shaq's sport, for short
6 Blue-green shade
10 Truant's letters
14 French middle school
15 Mao Tse-___
16 Cry of despair
17 Open courtyards
18 Conceal
19 Tool collections
20 ___-Magnon
21 Birds of prey
24 English article
25 Rock group with painted faces
27 Shatner's "___ Kill"
28 Homes on the range?
30 Cher movie of 1985
31 Suffix with Capri
32 Porsche model
33 Edmonton's prov.
34 Author Deighton
35 Steal gas, in a way
36 Pep rally cry
37 Loser

39 Wrath
40 Prepares to pray
42 Bolt's companion
43 Conclusions
44 Ford flop
45 U-turn from WNW
46 Versifier
47 Group of four
49 "___ walks in beauty ..."
50 Field measure
51 Stray
52 Noisy canine activity
55 "A Nightmare on ___ Street"
56 "... ___ saw Elba"
58 Noggin
59 "Get ___!" ("Stop panicking!")
61 Certain deer
62 Bank offering: Abbr.
63 Gem
64 Mlle. in Madrid
65 Prefix with stat
66 Baffling problem

DOWN

1 Under-the-counter traders
2 One way to test

3 Like 150 to 151, address-wise
4 Hawaiian garland
5 Tea unit
6 Jocks
7 Accelerate
8 Reverse
9 Secretive sort?
10 "Fine!" NASA-style
11 Beast with two horns
12 Debatable
13 Flips out
22 Bikini and others
23 Become established
26 Reggae relative
29 Young seal
35 Shiny fabric
37 Ease
38 Enter hastily
41 Auction ending
43 Org. that monitors emissions
48 Exclude
53 Poland's Walesa
54 Pant
57 O.T. book
60 Pontiac muscle car of yore

150

1	2	3	4	5		6	7	8	9		10	11	12	13
14						15					16			
17						18					19			
20				21	22				23		24			
25			26		27			28		29				
30					31				32					
33					34			35						
36				37			38				39			
40			41			42				43				
44						45				46				
47				48		49				50				
51				52		53			54		55			
56			57		58				59	60				
61					62				63					
64					65				66					

151

Thematic
Crosswords

94 BE MY HEALTHY VALENTINE

ACROSS

1 Jaworski or Trotsky
5 Sit-ups strengthen them
8 Times to stay awake
14 Art Carney role on *The Honeymooners*
16 Cry of accomplishment
17 Start of a healthy Valentine Day quip
19 Card player's cry
20 Beatty of *Network*
21 Hair goo
22 *Ben-Hur* novelist Wallace
23 Use weasel words
25 AFL counterpart
26 Bart Simpson's sis
27 More of the quip
30 Whisker trimmer
31 Explosive letters
32 Serve to be replayed
33 Move to the right
34 More of the quip
36 When mammoths lived
40 Stock market abbr.
41 Ands and buts alternatives
44 Word with school or bracelet
45 More of the quip
47 They're ruined by runs
48 Caesar of comedy

49 Dog, to a mailman's leg, perhaps
51 PC key
52 *A League of Their ___*
53 "Catch ya later!"
55 Corp. head
56 End of the quip
60 Used a silver tongue
61 That's your final answer, in addition
62 Bounce on one's knee, as a baby
63 ___ *longa, vita brevis*
64 Computer data unit

DOWN

1 Vivien of *Gone With the Wind*
2 Nervous to the max
3 Endlessly, seemingly
4 Armistice mo.
5 "Don't look ___!"
6 Hopalong Cassidy portrayer William
7 Weekend TV fare
8 The V of VCR
9 Pastoral poem
10 Gerard or Hodges
11 Think the world of
12 Keeps a-going
13 Patrick of *Star Trek: The Next Generation*

15 "Walk Away ___"
18 Opposed to, in Dogpatch
24 Clock-setting std.
25 Morsels for Morris
26 Young chap
28 Smurf-colored
29 TKO caller
30 ICU staffers
33 Rainfall measurement
34 Cinema trigram
35 Part of FWIW
36 Crane of *The Legend of Sleepy Hollow*
37 Illness prevented by water sanitation
38 Kodak's creator
39 "___ we having fun yet?"
41 Here, in Quebec
42 Municipality of Easy Street?
43 Make fun of
45 Be a squealer or a caroler
46 Film critic Roger
48 Stockholm dweller
50 Esther of *Good Times*
52 Hurler Hershiser
53 Become fuzzy
54 Candied veggies
57 From Jan. 1 to now
58 Greenwood's "God Bless the ___"
59 Large clump

154

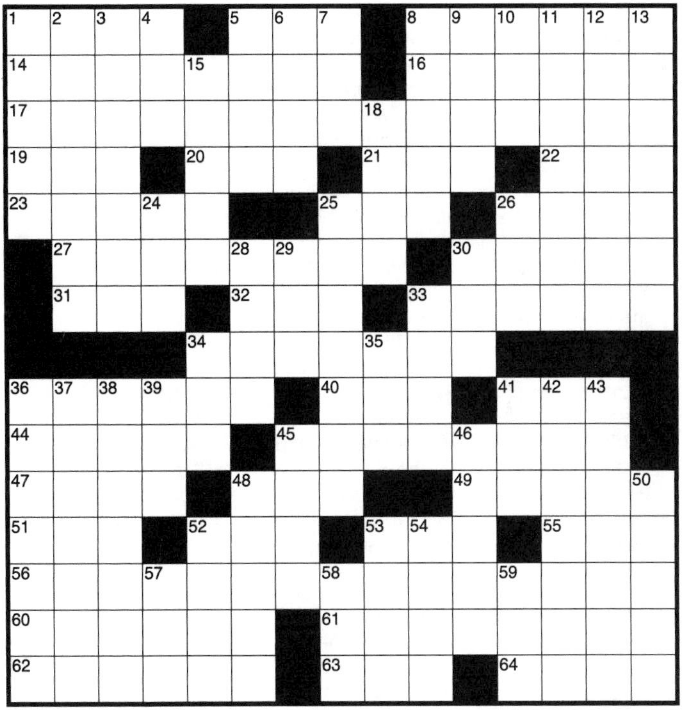

95 SHAKE IT ALL ABOUT

ACROSS
1 Abraham's almost-sacrificed son
6 Hose trouble
10 Yankee legend Rizzuto
14 Donkey Kong fighter
15 Circle of angels?
16 Brat Pack member Rob
17 Backup strategy
18 Foot part
19 Three oceans touch it
20 With 28-Across, truly repent
23 Poker prize
26 Lobster eggs
27 Cats and dogs
28 See 20-Across
30 Meas. of academic excellence
31 Bathtub stain
32 Leader after Indian independence
35 Librarian's admonition
38 Theme of this puzzle
42 Singer Yoko
43 Easterners on a ranch
44 Dandy's partner
45 Feel out of sorts
46 Interrupt
48 Freight train component

52 Cause of Apr. angst
53 Follower of Red or Dead
54 Proper charity
57 Ready and willing partner
58 Cartoon canine
59 Apartment dweller that pays no rent
63 Resolve, with "out"
64 Rembrandt works
65 For paid and unpaid players
66 Legislators make them
67 Haiku writer
68 Materials deposited in rivers

DOWN
1 Rambunctious child
2 Mineo of *Exodus*
3 Parseghian of Notre Dame fame
4 "I ___ Got Nobody"
5 James of *Our Man Flint*
6 Classic Alan Ladd western
7 Not, before "a one"
8 Tennessee aluminum town
9 Do without food
10 Red Cross supply

11 Old Testament book
12 "___ Survive"
13 Turns the pages of, with "through"
21 TV host Serling
22 Tear to pieces
23 Don of game shows
24 Hunter of the stars
25 The Lone Ranger's sidekick
29 "That's disgusting!"
32 Show agreement
33 Scratch
34 "For ___ a jolly good ..."
35 Short comic sketches
36 Skater Sonja
37 Villain in *The Lion King*
39 Official decree
40 Circular '50s fad
41 Frequently
45 Capital of Greece
46 Pal, rapper-style
47 Seizes illegally
48 Easily damaged
49 The Scales, in the zodiac
50 Shining
51 CB, for one
52 That is, to Caesar
55 Cairo river
56 Singer Amos
60 MSN alternative
61 Felix or Fritz
62 ___ *Pinafore*

96 **SHOW TUNES**

ACROSS

1 Ross MacDonald gumshoe Archer
4 *The Power of Positive Thinking* author Norman Vincent ___
9 "___ to Be You"
14 Shade of blond
15 Robin Hood portrayer Flynn
16 Tune from *Guys and Dolls*
17 Half of a rum drink
18 Shaq of the NBA
19 Type of toast
20 Tune from *Sweet Charity*
23 "Man of a Thousand Faces" Chaney
24 Rick's *Casablanca* love
25 Pesters
28 Group on horseback, maybe
31 Drained through a channel
34 Moo ___ pork
35 Title tune of a Rodgers and Hammerstein musical
38 *The Lion King* hero
41 Busy one
42 Pesters
43 Tune from *Annie*
45 Underlings of a capt.
46 Translates from plaintext

48 Former Israeli defense minister Moshe
50 Most red in the middle
52 Corp. heads
54 Baseball's Mel
55 Tune from *Show Boat*
61 Put up with
64 Baseball Hall of Famer Combs
65 Jackie's second spouse
66 Tune from *42nd Street*
67 TV show with Mr. T, with *The*
68 Cambridge U.
69 Brew, in a teapot
70 They meet at a center
71 Dispensable sweet treat

DOWN

1 Moussaka meat
2 Morales of *Resurrection Blvd.*
3 Tory rival
4 Tune from *Funny Girl*
5 Sea eagles
6 Gladiatorial sites
7 Put ammo into
8 *Vogue* competitor
9 Belief system
10 Wed. preceder
11 Title tune from a musical based on *The Matchmaker*
12 The ___ Dukes (Ted Nugent's old rock group)

13 College bigwigs
21 Family reunion attendee
22 Complain bitterly
26 CSA member
27 Classic pop
28 "Hey, over here!"
29 Louisville's river
30 Tune from *Porgy and Bess*
32 Lerner's *Camelot* collaborator
33 Luau music maker
36 Introduction to physics?
37 Org.
39 Word with crushing or china
40 Jumps electrodes
41 Weightlifter's pride, slangily
44 Prefix with tiller
47 Terror-stricken
48 Tune from *The Sound of Music*
49 Faulkner title start
50 They all lead to Rome, they say
51 Trip to the plate
53 Zhou ___
56 Shakespearean king
57 ___ Hari of espionage
58 Seductive woman
59 Canal of Sal
60 Big name in hotels or crackers
62 Wallace of *E.T.*
63 Three letters for the sixth sense

158

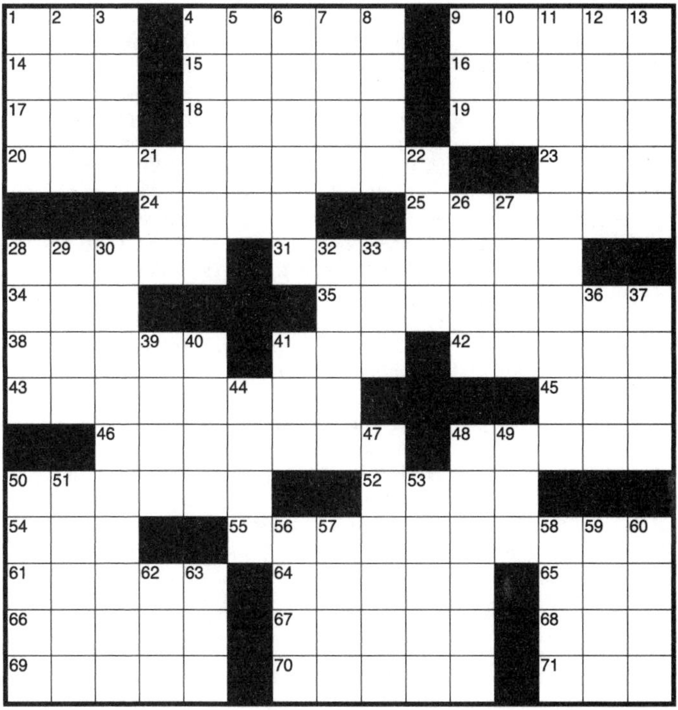

97 THREE IN ONE

ACROSS

1 Accustoms to food other than milk
6 Explode, with "up"
10 ___ and a Baby (Ted Danson flick)
14 Cow in commercials
15 Pear-shaped instrument
16 All-night bash
17 Border just off the coast
19 Eyewitness's words
20 Low-cut shoes
21 Cell terminal
22 Like the shortest hole on the course
26 007, for one
27 Hancock, to the Declaration of Independence
28 Basketball's coach Rupp
30 Antony of Rome
31 Arafat of the PLO
32 Meek as a lamb
36 Bonk, in the Bible
37 Where drives begin
38 Synthetic material
40 Chance for a tennis triumph
42 Submarine "window," for short
43 Cowardly Lion portrayer Bert
44 Daze

45 Hip-high boots
48 Sass
50 E-mail command
51 Descend ladder and wed
52 Blade that's sometimes rattled
54 WKRP costar with Howard
55 Coat, vest, and pants
60 Drink in big gulps
61 Columnist Barrett
62 Audacity
63 Sombrero and fedora
64 Watch-winding knob
65 Tucker of country music

DOWN

1 Start of a Christmas carol
2 Nightmare street
3 "___ was saying ..."
4 Nothing
5 Ooze gradually
6 Lighter-than-air vehicle
7 Like gravy, maybe
8 Mayberry jail frequenter
9 In need of a towel
10 Entertainment under a tent
11 Marsha of The Goodbye Girl
12 Get out of
13 More recent
18 Teeming with growth

21 Mail delivered by plane
22 Forks over
23 2nd or 6th president
24 WWII riveter
25 Oinkers in a children's story
27 Unstamped enc.
29 Get ready
30 Track event
32 Whoop-de-do
33 Rooster's sweetheart
34 Upgrade or downgrade
35 Biker's invitation
39 Single-minded enthusiast
41 Wonder words
44 Write standards
45 Raquel of Myra Breckinridge
46 Island state's greeting
47 "Hole" wheat pastry?
48 "Mule Train" singer
49 Letter-shaped metal piece
52 TV commercial
53 Money for the landlord
55 Reading, 'riting, and 'rithmetic
56 Body of salt water
57 Decaf dispenser, sometimes
58 Wrigley Field feature
59 Beverage from a bag

98 PRETTY CUTE

ACROSS

1 Diamond judges
5 Wide-awake
10 "___ only trying to help"
14 Spot under the North Star
15 "When donkeys fly!" so to speak
16 Tat opener
17 Healthy vibrations?
19 It gets fired up
20 Baseball boo-boo
21 Have poor posture
23 ___ Mahal
24 Princess toppers
26 Howard of the Three Stooges
27 Sign of a hit
28 NBC weekend comedy show, briefly
29 Badgers a cartoon bunny?
33 Young ladies' org.
35 "And how!"
36 Conical tent
37 Most muscular
41 Former NFL coach Don
44 Forensic evidence
45 Off-road transport, briefly
48 Pica or elite?
52 Row, row, row your boat

54 Oval-shaped food
55 Old-fashioned preposition
56 Taste to test
58 Balloon contents, maybe
59 Nickname for 60-Down
62 England's Wars of the ___
63 Edible part of a nut
65 Crushed earth?
67 Comes to a halt
68 Greeting for Dolly
69 Actress/singer Adams
70 Offend the olfactories
71 Blazer material
72 Place, as in a tournament

DOWN

1 Underdog victories
2 Tying to the dock
3 They usually end in "s"
4 Mister of Mexico
5 Adviser Landers
6 People of the Lion's sign
7 ___ eye (bad luck look)
8 Job seeker's summary
9 Earthquake omen

10 Tick off
11 Puts off going to bed
12 On the loose
13 Silicon Valley city
18 Humdrum
22 Harmful insects
25 Soft drink
30 Haul with a line
31 East Indian language
32 Letter after alpha
34 Competent
38 Bolero composer
39 Suffix with hero or Paul
40 Really enjoys, with "up"
41 Clam, pot, or ship
42 Practice of good health
43 Improved version
46 On the deck
47 Harper or Bertinelli
49 Properly
50 Sketched again
51 It's almost one meter
53 Took five
57 Methods
60 Senator from North Carolina
61 Type of log
64 Condescending cluck
66 Doze off

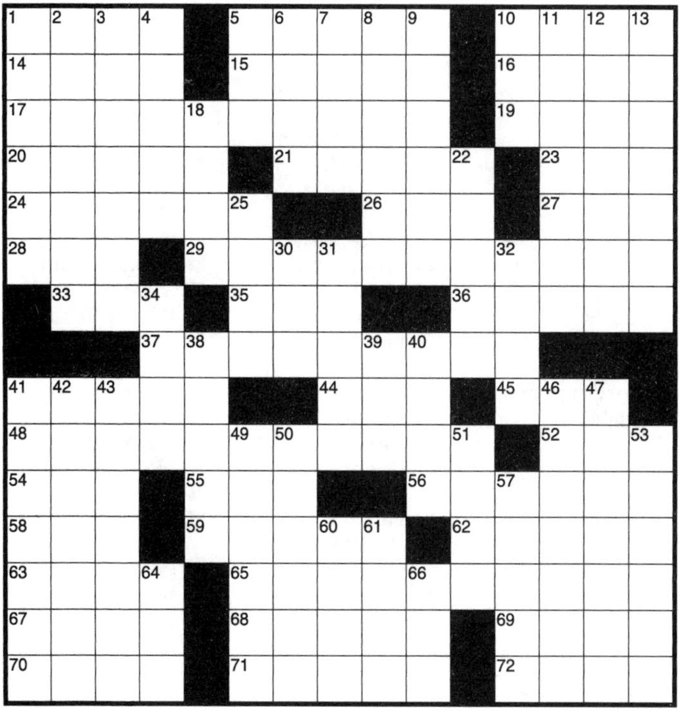

99 COAT OF MANY COLORS

ACROSS

1 Most populous continent
5 Teheran's country
9 "___ forgive our debtors"
13 Highway entrance or exit
14 Rowlands of *Hope Floats*
15 Birds' facts-of-life partners
16 Prepares to shoot
17 Falls behind
18 Let it stand, to editors
19 Working-class
22 Letters before an alias
23 Charged particle
24 Plate by the catcher
25 Strong point
27 Belief statement
29 Lion or leopard
30 Silver-tongued speaker
34 Says further
35 Song with the same melody as "What Child Is This?"
38 Takes to court
39 Part of a compass
40 Spruces up
42 State o' potato
46 Out on a limb
47 *Othello* villain
50 White House souvenir
51 Heat meas.
52 Host of a '50s comedy show
55 Where spills should land
57 Drape holders
58 Last word in a threat
59 Snaky swimmers
60 Excessive supply
61 One-armed bandit
62 Pulled a gun
63 Nobel Institute city
64 Babies in blue

DOWN

1 Like our numerals
2 Sinbad, for one
3 Protected from germs
4 Church section
5 House of ice
6 Royal domain
7 Go fishing
8 Project Mercury's org.
9 Tummy muscles
10 Amount withheld
11 Saturdays and Sundays
12 Large tracts of land
20 Odd job
21 Sally Field's *Norma ___*
26 Worked relentlessly
28 Brings to ruin
29 Savage of *The Wonder Years*
31 Landers and Sothern
32 Mao ___-tung
33 Hispanic "Hooray!"
35 More culpable
36 Boost
37 Capone capturer Ness
38 Pierced with a point
41 Suffix with auction
43 Brother of Artemis
44 Muppet-maker Jim
45 Beginnings
47 Blindly admired people
48 Choreographer Paula
49 Relish
53 Logician's word
54 Lass in a Hardy tale
56 U-turn from NNE

100 C+

ACROSS

1 Threads worn in beds
8 Listen in electronically
15 Nickel or neon
16 Steel foundry input
17 Lawyers that fight and scratch for you?
19 Red-ink figure
20 Knighted actor Guinness
21 Trials and tribulations
22 Really impressed, with "away"
23 Hosp. worker
25 Gets around
29 Leaves, as on an island
33 Saint of Missouri
34 Capital near the pyramids
36 Woody's ex
37 Malfunctioned like a mouse?
40 "Y" wearer
41 Cake advocate Antoinette
42 Ten percent levy
43 Dull routine
45 Areas of dense underbrush
46 Rock composer Brian
47 WWII General Bradley
49 On ___ (without a contract)

52 Bit of news
53 Sparkle
57 Flatter singer Patsy?
61 Cold comfort for a bruise
62 "Nothing can be done now!"
63 The Gobi and the Mohave
64 Got hot under the collar

DOWN

1 Sound of thunder or laughter
2 Kind of sax
3 Nozzles in a hot tub
4 "Famous" cookie maker
5 Prefix for maid
6 Historical records
7 Memorial stone
8 Neighbor of Minn.
9 Gershwin lyricist
10 Go bad
11 Town near Beverly Hills
12 Fee paid at a bridge
13 Asian inland sea
14 Supporters of the congregation?
18 Longbow wood

22 Wedding party member
23 Dr. Zhivago's love
24 Exam official
25 Kind of statesman
26 "Presto!"
27 IRS examination
28 Hullabaloo
29 Amp attachment
30 Misses
31 Recess for a statuette
32 "Land ___!"
34 Delicious discard
35 Onassis, to Jackie
38 Texas city
39 Half of a kisser
44 Food formula
45 Flirted with, with "to"
47 Giant Mel
48 Conductor Zubin
49 Tried to avoid a tag
50 Walk the waiting room
51 Potato bumps
52 Squirts like a squid
53 Reese's *Legally Blonde* role
54 Tall tale teller
55 It goes to pot
56 Require
58 Prefix with heel
59 Halloween mo.
60 Gear tooth

1	2	3	4	5	6	7		8	9	10	11	12	13	14
15								16						
17							18							
19					20						21			
				22					23	24				
25	26	27	28					29				30	31	32
33						34	35					36		
37				38							39			
40				41						42				
43			44						45					
			46				47	48						
49	50	51				52					53	54	55	56
57				58	59					60				
61							62							
63							64							

101 EXPLETIVE DELETED

ACROSS
1 Utterly awful
8 Cairo's continent
14 Eavesdropping device
15 *Julius Caesar* role
16 Rhett's line censored?
18 Trial run
19 River to the Caspian
20 *Night* writer Wiesel
21 Silica mineral
22 Washer's partner
23 Knocked off
27 Long car, for short
29 On a pedestal
31 Belgrade resident
36 Anti-draft line censored?
38 Calf catcher
39 Less original
40 Stumble
42 Comics witch Broom-___
43 Carved column
47 Meal-in-bed supporter
49 Met moment
50 Chase flies
51 Melodious Fitzgerald

55 Baseball musical censored?
58 Minerva, on the Acropolis
59 "Foiled again!" crier?
60 Type of shoe fastener
61 Site famous for scrolls

DOWN
1 Foolish fellow
2 Duck down
3 Winged youth of myth
4 Bottled (up)
5 Addams Family cousin
6 Touch base
7 Kind of notebook
8 United Steelworkers leader I.W. ___
9 Title for a brother
10 More fresh
11 Geographical "boot"
12 Physicist Marie
13 Moore's TV boss of old
17 Porter's burden
21 Lacking in variety
22 Oz visitor

23 Children's author Roald
24 Gray matter output
25 Shrinks, e.g.
26 Ticks off
28 Kitty cries
30 Procrastinator's opposite
32 Sons of, in Hebrew
33 "___ never work!"
34 Getting on in years
35 *You've Got Mail* director Ephron
37 Squirm
41 Talked up?
43 Egyptian Peace Nobelist
44 Paces in races
45 Black billiard ball
46 Saloon serving
48 Showing surprise
50 Go ballistic
51 Scratched (out)
52 Waikiki wreaths
53 ___ majesty
54 Dog of the screen
56 Man-mission connector
57 PBS benefactor

102 DOES MY HMO COVER THIS?

ACROSS

1 It keeps your lobe warm
8 Joked with
14 "Good gracious!"
15 *Tinker, Tailor, Soldier, Spy* author
16 With 37- and 59-Across, become ticked off
17 Alcohol derivative in paint
18 Had a hunch that
20 Goat tot
21 Heflin and Johnson
23 Kennedy's title: Abbr.
24 Hive hummers
25 Björn of tennis
26 Per-species limit for Noah
28 One of a birth pair
30 Shade tree
31 Pillow covers
33 Cotton Club singer Waters
36 Army NCO
37 See 16-Across
39 U-turn from WNW
40 Tended
42 Book of maps
43 *One Day ___ Time*
44 The Hawkeye State
46 Use oars

47 Horse of early TV
48 Tube for water
50 Hawaiian necklace
52 Palm fruit
53 What "10" may mean: Abbr.
54 *Babbitt* author Lewis
57 Swept with a small broom
59 See 16-Across
63 A form of bowling
64 Tolerated
65 Keyboard instruments with pipes
66 14-line poems

DOWN

1 Golden goose goodie
2 Pub offering
3 "Horsefeathers!"
4 Cooking in oil
5 City on the Rhone
6 Border on
7 Lima's nation
8 Not long past
9 On the rocks
10 Go on offense on the diamond
11 Crushed spirit
12 Comical Kovacs
13 Property papers
15 After the appointed time
19 Type of exercise
21 River to the Caspian

22 Persuasion with pressure
24 Chomped into
25 Porgy's lady
26 E'en if
27 "Papa ___ Rollin' Stone"
29 Antiprohibition-ists
31 Winter precipitation
32 Song for a single singer
34 Lipstick-maker Lauder
35 Metal used in fishing weights
38 Labor org. for makers of cars
41 It tests the water
45 People from other planets
47 Put ashore as punishment
48 Instruction book genre
49 Earth tone
51 Means justification, to some
52 Type of mustard
54 It covers your body
55 Tosses gently
56 Curly do
58 Site for three men in a tub
60 '50s prez
61 Tennis court divider
62 Football scores: Abbr.

103 VERBAL AGREEMENT

ACROSS
1 Thin-waisted insect
5 Spiders' quarters
9 Companions of crafts
13 Pro ___
14 What your nose knows
16 Layer of paint
17 Cobbler's agreement?
19 Biggest brass instrument
20 "By the ___ Get to Phoenix"
21 Knight's agreement?
23 Left out, as letters
25 Fail to grip the road
26 "How ___ love thee?"
27 Renter of rooms
28 Work area or dog
30 Give up
32 Teachers' org.
33 Beginning of a prayer
36 Put two and two together, literally
37 Shepherd's agreement?
40 Move, as an eyelash
42 Beer mug
43 Humor magazine
46 Like an animal-friendly society
49 Get dressed, with "up"
50 4th mo.

51 In the distance
52 Swamp reptile, for short
55 It has one eye that can't see
57 Optometrist's agreement?
60 High-ranking horse
61 Its vehicles aren't UFOs
62 Blacksmith's agreement?
64 Picnic spoilers
65 Melody rapidity
66 Comedian Johnson
67 Eye problem
68 Flower of the Kennedys?
69 Discouraging words

DOWN
1 Vote for one not on the ballot
2 Winnie-the-Pooh creator
3 Physical endurance
4 "Knocked" on the door, like Lassie
5 Auxiliary for flyers
6 Boy with bow and arrows
7 Natasha's cartoon comrade
8 Smug smile
9 First part of a play
10 Brought together, with "up"

11 Prurient periodical
12 The Bee Gees' "___ Alive"
15 Top floor
18 Stay out of sight
22 Nabokov novel
24 Friend-winner Carnegie
29 Head honcho
31 Big tub
34 Turn in, with "on"
35 Cut calories
37 Guesstimate letters
38 "My Heart Will Go On" singer Celine
39 Send to the tummy
40 Lighter than water
41 Pardon from an authority
43 Amber-colored wine
44 Galore
45 Deepens, as a waterway
46 Villains in *The Lion King*
47 Sgt., for one
48 German Surrealist Max
53 Shade of yellow
54 Mario not of Nintendo
56 Hawke of *Training Day*
58 Lawsuit
59 Agents, for short
63 Caviar, before processing

172

1	2	3	4		5	6	7	8			9	10	11	12
13					14				15		16			
17				18							19			
20						21				22				
23					24		25					26		
27				28		29				30		31		
32					33			34	35			36		
			37							38	39			
	40	41				42						43	44	45
46				47	48			49				50		
51				52		53	54		55		56			
57			58					59		60				
61					62				63					
64					65						66			
67					68						69			

104 BACK-TO-BACK VICTORIES

ACROSS

1 Rational religion
6 Kind of admiral
10 Type of pattern or pilot
14 On one's toes
15 Earthenware jar
16 Scat legend Fitzgerald
17 "Jean-etic" material
18 Rations
20 Use a ballot
22 When the show must go on
23 Word on a palm reader's shingle
26 Playing for ___
27 Knight's apprentice
28 Church leader
31 Hall's singing partner
32 Covered with vines
33 Initial serving at lunch?
36 What tots are taught
37 Shrewd
38 Ice sheet
39 "¡Olé!" north of the border
40 Humphrey's nickname
41 Work your fingers to the bone
42 Piece with staggered melodies
43 High-traction shoes
44 High, flat areas
47 Had a broken heart
49 Teheran dweller
52 Norwegian king
53 Tube audience
55 Two-masted vessel
59 Hill in Jerusalem
60 Lake of Commodore Perry's victory
61 Hardly award-winning writing
62 Concerning
63 Lead a ___ life
64 Sesame Street grouch

DOWN

1 June honoree
2 Fleecy female
3 Singer Janis
4 Underwear
5 Autobiography
6 Drive in Beverly Hills
7 Connecticut collegian
8 A, as in Edison
9 Beatle George's sitarist friend
10 Wobble
11 Pitcher of milk?
12 Mild recession
13 Watergate evidence
19 Got on the nerves of
21 Mao ___-tung
23 Gulf off the Red Sea
24 Type of treat
25 Stationary acceleration
27 Head for the heavens
29 Not recorded
30 She played the elder Partridge sister
32 Enemy of the Moor
33 "The Tyger" poet William
34 Went gaga over
35 Shirts with slogans, often
37 Gun's offspring?
38 Old cars
40 Ellington contemporary
41 Address
42 Incisor's neighbor
43 S of RSVP
44 Gaynor of South Pacific
45 Nixon nemesis Sam
46 Smack your lips over
48 They're often purchased in dozens
50 Totally blown away
51 Elephantine Wolfe
54 Fix, as an election
56 Nervous twitch
57 Books balancer
58 H of HRH

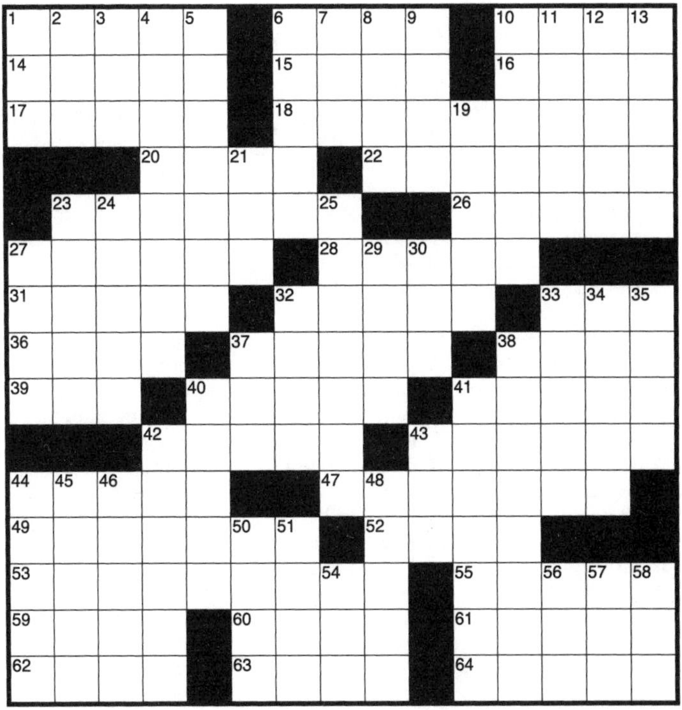

105 MIXED CHOCOLATES

ACROSS
1 His parents raised Cain
5 Computer inserts
10 Got an A on
14 Dracula portrayer Lugosi
15 Loose from restraint
16 Variety of herring
17 Nat King's salary?
19 One-third of a war film title
20 Beatles' drummer
21 Secretly
23 Did a take-off on
26 Roll call response
27 Marks over é and è
31 Harrison of *Doctor Dolittle*
32 Invoice col.
35 Treasure chests, e.g.?
37 Hose shade
38 Slatted storage box
39 Legendary sleeper
40 Give a tongue-lashing to
41 Fairy tale's first word
42 "Get DiCaprio, already!"?
44 Mount Saint Helens fallout
45 "Holy cow!"
46 Trigger man
47 List-shortening abbr.
49 "Take ___ leave it!"
50 Facecloths
53 Bring to an end
58 TV lawyer McBeal
59 Chic swindlers?
62 ___ and board
63 Bert's buddy, on *Sesame Street*
64 Write hastily, with "off"
65 Seeger or Sampras
66 Take care of
67 "Drat it!"

DOWN
1 Kindergarten stuff
2 Cop's milieu
3 Wordless part in *Born Free*
4 Bert of *The Wizard of Oz*
5 Batman and Robin, e.g.
6 Ltd., in the U.S.
7 Got to one's feet
8 Pottery oven
9 Does a slow burn
10 Disk-shaped flower
11 Selected one young horse?
12 Judge Warren
13 *Saving Private Ryan* event
18 Half-conscious state
22 Put the whammy on
24 School org.
25 Third-party account
27 Big name in kitchen foil
28 Woes for toes
29 Where athletic leaders park?
30 Suffix with cigar
31 Meal
33 1957 hit for the Bobbettes
34 House of Henry VIII
36 Soda-drinker's sound
37 Sound on the rebound
40 Shrivel with heat
42 Offers a shoulder to cry on
43 Howe'er
45 Armed conflict
48 Stew seasoning
49 "This ___ of Those Moments" (song from *Yentl*)
50 Bend out of shape
51 Lotion additive
52 Environmentalists' pal Al
54 Indecent
55 Diamond Head locale
56 Recipe directive
57 X-Games airer
60 Left in a hurry, with "out"
61 Corporate VIP

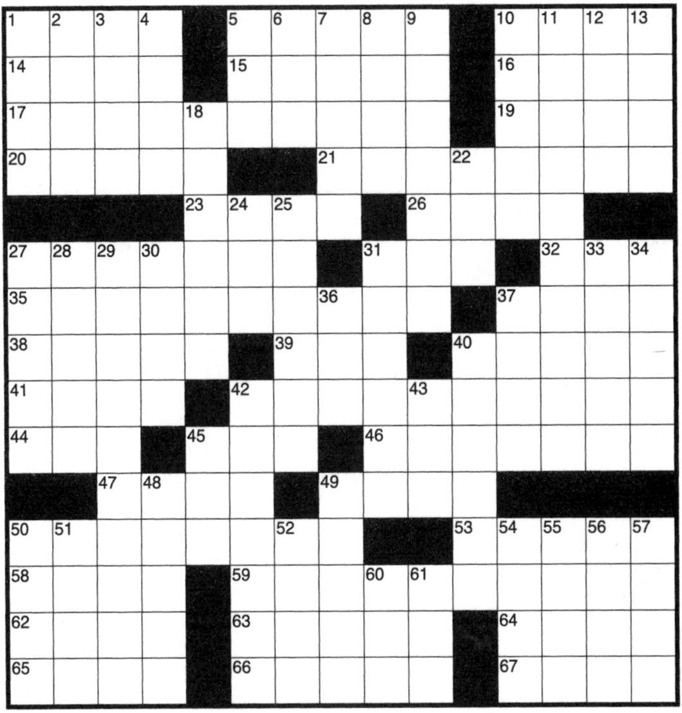
1
2
3
4
5
6
7
8
9
10
11
12
13
14
15
16
17
18
19
20
21
22
23
24
25
26
27
28
29
30
31
32
33
34
35
36
37
38
39
40
41
42
43
44
45
46
47
48
49
50
51
52
53
54
55
56
57
58
59
60
61
62
63
64
65
66
67

106 DIGITAL DICTIONARY

ACROSS

1 Bricklayer
6 Speedway competition
10 Droopy
14 Foil brand
15 Sea bordering Kazakhstan
16 Moslem official
17 Round missile at the Nerf Olympics?
19 Place for an altar
20 Neighbor of Syr.
21 Mate, in Montreal
22 Least verbose
24 Soul singer Redding
26 Sparkling Italian wine
28 Like Poe stories
29 December delivery man
31 Difficult car journey?
33 Some are vital
35 Christopher Robin's pal
36 Spy novelist Deighton
37 Flying cave dwellers
39 Naysayers' words
41 Like a treacherous sidewalk
44 Traveler to Cathay
46 Agassi's "weapon"

50 Mickey's and Minnie's apartments?
53 "Death Be Not Proud" poet
54 Ice cream drinks
55 Bench-presser's pride
57 In need of stitching
58 Brought into play
60 Tiresome grind
62 Comedian Bill, to friends
63 Site of annual floods
64 Reattach with adhesive?
67 Powder on the slopes
68 Tennis legend Arthur
69 Deceive
70 They go with bacon
71 Watered down
72 ^

DOWN

1 Gangster
2 Elite athlete
3 Making points
4 Caveman of comics
5 California wine valley
6 Salad slice
7 Meyers of *Kate and Allie*

8 Like a heartburn-resistant stomach
9 Sommer of *A Shot in the Dark*
10 Apartment owner, e.g.
11 Expose to danger
12 Epistle
13 Child of 12 years, for one
18 Singer Sumac
23 Carrot-top
25 Wild guess
27 Kind of dance
30 Foot with three syllables
32 *Let's Make a Deal* option
34 Point on a metro map
38 Willy-nilly
40 Kilt wearer
41 Staggering
42 Persuading gently
43 Christmas fireplace fuel
45 Pindaric poem
47 Entrance attachment
48 On the way
49 Sawbuck
51 Spreads around
52 Monitor part
56 Deli hero
59 State, in French
61 Sprinkle after a shower
65 Letter voiced by a Greek giant?
66 KGB counterpart

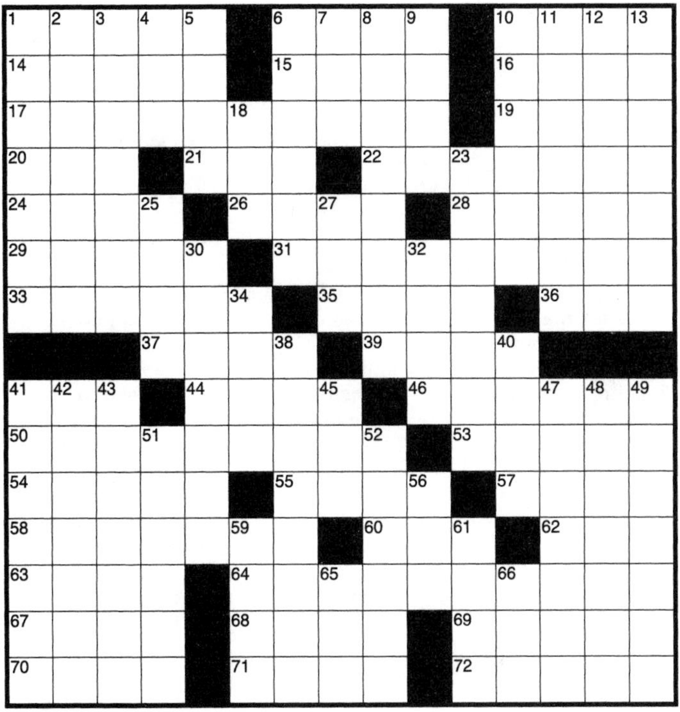

107 NOT NECESSARILY WINTER

ACROSS
1 C&W star McEntire
5 Steel girder
10 Pink-slips
14 Periods of time
15 Poverty-stricken
16 Very much
17 *That Was the Week That Was* host
19 Meter maid in a Beatles song
20 1860s abbr.
21 Alternative to a sail
22 Airplane garage, so to speak
24 *Days of ___ Lives*
25 Whomp, old-style
28 "Death ___ Proud"
29 Opera highlight
31 First to break the sound barrier
33 Hydrocarbon suffix
34 Blood and sweat companions
36 Overwhelm
38 Sound of a dove
40 Govt. ecology group
41 Precariously situated
47 Shy
51 Actress Vardalos of *My Big Fat Greek Wedding*

52 Type of cup used as an award
54 Sprinter's assignment
55 Very perceptive
57 Pacific island group
59 "I ___ Rhythm"
60 Response to "Gracias," maybe
62 Taxing mo.
63 Palindromic preposition
64 ABA members
65 Corrupt pols' accounts
69 Waste allowance
70 Group of deputies
71 Editor's comment
72 Jane of fiction
73 More rational
74 Corn stalk attachments

DOWN
1 British soldier
2 Where the rubber meets the paper
3 Area around Munich
4 "Do ___ do"
5 Shame
6 Small fruits
7 Fair hiring letters
8 Notices in the classified section

9 Old wives' tale
10 Chili con ___
11 Made straight
12 Zip
13 One of the best players, generally
18 Half of *cuatro*
23 Curt
26 Catch some rays
27 I, to Claudius
30 Curve over a door
32 She sheep
35 Made dirty
37 Manicurist's target
39 Lennon's lady
41 At the movies, perhaps
42 "Close, but no cigar"
43 Bronx cheer giver
44 OR hookups
45 Info-gathering org.
46 As a group
48 Purplish red
49 Properly arranged
50 Is unable to stand?
53 Ground squirrel
56 Take a nibble
58 Canine comment
61 Nile biters
66 Mauna ___
67 Fleet of Amer.
68 Take advantage of

180

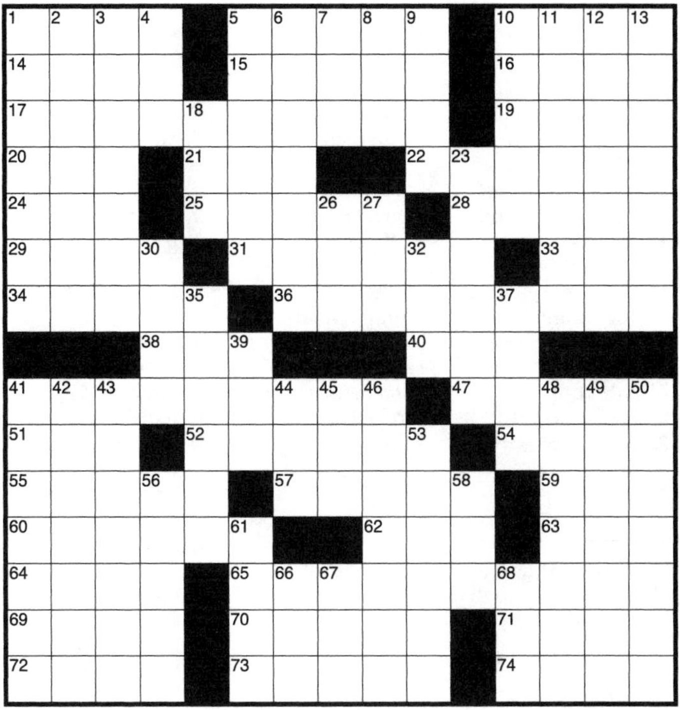

108 FAUX DIAMOND

ACROSS

1 Oolong and pekoe
5 Gem weight unit
10 Drinks ordered with a "Yo ho ho"
14 Johnson of "Laugh-In" fame
15 Tolerate
16 Coup d'___
17 Cake mix container?
19 Colorado resort town
20 Sand bar
21 Low blow?
23 Continent north of Afr.
24 Bottle cap remover
26 Likely
27 Kids' card game
28 Gave some lip to
32 Building wing
33 It shades the eyes
35 Paris subway
36 Pd. or unpd. sabbatical
37 List deductions
39 Outer edge
40 Opening section
42 Type of demonstration
43 Skater's surface
44 From time immemorial
46 Mo. of Labor Day
47 Rap sheet info
48 Agreements with landlords

50 Actor's signal
51 Bad advice?
54 Passover bread
56 Early lessons
57 Personal cache?
61 Beginning of a court plea
62 Mistake
63 The smallest bills
64 *Dragonheart* voice Connery
65 Washington team, for short
66 Taye Diggs musical

DOWN

1 Ring on a drink can
2 Chunks of history
3 Where chowhounds excel?
4 Begin a journey
5 Cosmologist Sagan
6 Crunch targets
7 Bone removed in Eden
8 Big name in digital software
9 Dallas dwellers
10 R in a car
11 Great Salt Lake site
12 Neighbor of Algeria
13 Undo a dele

18 Mr. Potato Head stick-on
22 Mariners
24 Desert watering holes
25 "I do," for one
26 As a companion
27 One-liner producer
29 Picket line?
30 *Fear of Flying* author Jong
31 Round roof
32 *On the Waterfront* director Kazan
33 Purple flower
34 Bar mitzvah and baptism
38 Compress, as a data file
41 Applies, as deodorant
45 Platforms for speakers
47 Mark Twain, to *Tom Sawyer*
49 Tiny bit of flame
50 Jazz aficionado
51 Breeze producers
52 Double-reed instrument
53 Pac-10 school
54 Next planet out after Earth
55 Serious sign
58 F of TGIF
59 Unfathomably long time
60 N.J. clock setting

109 BUYING OPTIONS

ACROSS

1 Raw fish dish
6 *Star Wars* genre
11 Is worthwhile
15 Words before a time
16 Ringlets of hair
17 No longer in port
18 Refinement
19 Disney mermaid
20 Command to Rover
21 Wool garment
24 *The Name of the Rose* author Umberto
25 SASE, e.g.
26 Seeds
28 Rupture
30 Go as far as
34 Lying flat
35 "Mentalist" Geller
37 It'll make you red in the face
39 Chemical suffix
40 Pattern of squares
43 At bat stat
45 Peter of Herman's Hermits
46 Cremona crowd?
47 Bonkers
49 Man to "tell 'em what they won"
51 Sign of mourning
55 Hinder

57 Newt
59 Letters from your parents?
60 Ambassador's sub
65 Blacken, as steak
66 Move without effort
67 Blackguard
68 Throw rocks at
69 Football Hall of Famer Merlin
70 Perfume compound
71 Some bookmarks
72 Unaided, as eyes
73 Sounds off like Simba

DOWN

1 Type of mom
2 Loosen, as shoes
3 Add salt
4 Corned beef concoction
5 Response to "Who's there?"
6 Hard to find
7 Quinine, for malaria
8 Where a pupil sits
9 Went by plane
10 Man and Wight
11 Congregation leader
12 Rock between Mars and Jupiter

13 Type of annual report
14 For example
22 Singer Caruso
23 Show up
27 "Got it?"
29 Head-slapper's cry
31 Stadium
32 Kitchen gadget
33 Center
36 Impressionist Pierre
38 Disembarked
40 Municipal government
41 Keystone character
42 Race the engine
43 Hosp. workers
44 Meat retailer
48 Intelligence, slangily
50 Answer the critics of
52 List of mistakes
53 "The nerve!"
54 High-tech beam makers
56 Provoke
58 Volunteer
61 Raines or Grasso
62 UFO shape, often
63 *Song of the South* syllables
64 Preceder of many words?
65 Computer heart: Abbr.

184

110 THE LOVE CONNECTION

ACROSS
1 Kind of PC monitor
4 Pear peeler
9 Violinist Stern
14 Galley slave's tool
15 City of Honshu
16 Marilyn's birth name
17 Do an impression of
18 Beside yourself with anger
19 Commercial writer, e.g.
20 Singer of "Love and Marriage"
23 Pago Pago site
24 Rock musician's fan
27 Lofty poems
30 In disagreement
32 Male lead in *Love Story*
37 Senate helper
38 Computer in *2001*
39 He wrote "The Love Song of J. Alfred Prufrock"
42 Cut down
43 St. Patrick's land
45 Singer of "Love Child"
47 Give counsel to
50 Garden smoother
51 Home of the Seahawks

54 Kind of scout or eye
58 Captain of *The Love Boat*
61 Bra part
64 "There!"
65 Deck (out)
66 Harbor in Hawaii
67 Fudd of cartoons
68 The Beach Boys' "Surfin' ___"
69 Uninvited pool guests
70 Salary increase
71 On the authority of

DOWN
1 Goofs off
2 *It Happened One Night* director
3 Have hopes
4 Round design
5 In the present condition
6 Sitarist Shankar
7 Barely making, with "out"
8 Detection system
9 Trapped by routine
10 Bubbly beverage
11 Weapon or limb
12 Simon and Garfunkel's "I ___ Rock"
13 Preserve
21 Palindromic time
22 Up ___ point

25 Boise's state
26 Borders
28 Printer's measures
29 Sunflower edible
31 Darns without swearing?
32 Actress Perlman
33 Areas around homes
34 Still in the game
35 2001 role for Will Smith
36 Whopper creator
40 Stop ___ dime
41 Exercise caution
44 Falls on the border of Canada
46 Kind of time
48 Paper fastener
49 PBS, for example
52 Onions partner
53 WWII plane ___ *Gay*
55 Start a new day
56 Almost ready for the tooth fairy
57 Father of Candice
59 *La Bohème* heroine
60 Pub potables
61 Mineral spring site
62 Address book no.
63 Newspaper, in slang

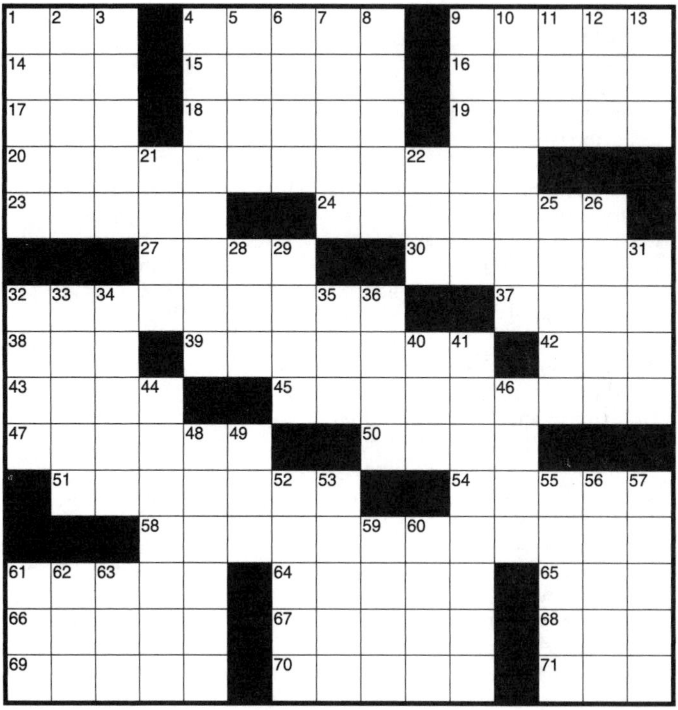

111 SERIES WINNERS

ACROSS

1 Feel one's way
6 Hung on to
10 Practices cartography
14 Type of tube
15 Something to think about
16 Stewpot
17 Prefix meaning "milk"
18 Clock sound
19 So-so
20 Correspondence times for a 1990 Series winner?
23 Audiophile's buy
25 Ending for opal
26 Bandleader Brown
27 Little lumps
28 Do pull-ups
31 Egypt's capital
33 MacGraw of *Love Story*
34 Madeline of *Blazing Saddles*
35 Last full mo. of summer
36 An esteemed 1969 Series winner?
42 Suffix with Siam
43 Courts
44 Neighbor of Miss.
45 Adds seasoning to
48 Ma of telephones
49 Czech or Serb
50 Sci-fi hoverer
51 Brooks of *Blazing Saddles*
53 *Little Women* writer Alcott
55 Planetary discovery by a 1995 Series winner?
59 Gesture with the hand
60 Jacob's first wife
61 Video game pioneer
64 "You can say that again!"
65 Dog tail?
66 "See ya!"
67 Sammy Davis Jr.'s ___ *Can*
68 Cyberspace companies: Abbr.
69 Type of preview or thief

DOWN

1 Bellows of *Ally McBeal*
2 Cell stuff, for short
3 One way to buy
4 Dwindles to nothing, with "out"
5 Wear away
6 Child's flying toy
7 Ready for press
8 Jelly thickener
9 Spoken for, as a seat
10 Type of swing or ring
11 Acid neutralizer
12 Golfer Gary
13 Lays down the law
21 Track down
22 Happens again
23 Went for a dip
24 It's tall when exaggerated
29 LBJ's veep
30 Thunderstruck
32 Formerly
34 ___, *Kate*
35 Historic Harlem theater
37 In opposition to prohibition
38 Neighbor of Ger.
39 Make legal
40 "What a shame!"
41 Obsidian source
45 Sandwich shop chain
46 Chalet shape
47 Bread portions
48 Censorship sounds
49 Babe Ruth, vis-à-vis swat
52 China's Zhou ___
54 Exams not on paper
56 "I came," to Caesar
57 Stinging insect
58 Word after "Knock, knock," in jokes
62 Stephen of *The Crying Game*
63 Get under the skin of

1	2	3	4	5		6	7	8	9		10	11	12	13
14						15					16			
17						18					19			
		20			21					22				
23	24							25				26		
27					28	29	30			31	32			
33				34					35					
36			37					38				39	40	41
			42				43					44		
45	46	47				48					49			
50				51	52				53	54				
55			56				57	58						
59					60					61			62	63
64					65					66				
67					68					69				

112 TEE SETS

ACROSS

1 Portfolio components
5 Moral code
10 Funny King
14 Dogpatch cartoonist
15 Hippo's zoo neighbor, perhaps
16 Ore source
17 Round snack
18 Play by Euripides
19 Language-neutral puzzle
20 "If this happens again ..."
22 Type of 50% discount
24 Sound character
25 They follow zetas
26 Cartoon spinach advocate
29 Pub hurlers
33 Quarterback's bid?
34 Brimless hat
35 Back from now
36 Season of giving up
37 Swiss capital
38 Cotton on a stick
39 Garfunkel or Linkletter
40 Tender spots
41 Cunning
42 Bamboozle verbally
44 Invented, as a phrase
45 Eight bits, but not a dollar
46 Bureau attachment?
47 Dancer Prowse
50 It stops a car
54 Sea bordering Uzbekistan
55 Rubbed the wrong way
57 Fraud
58 German Marx
59 Noble objective
60 Diarist Frank
61 Lodge members
62 Mexican minister
63 Touches with a baseball

DOWN

1 Clicked image
2 Steakhouse pink
3 High point
4 Quick assessment
5 White fur
6 Phrases with TT, in this puzzle
7 Keep under wraps
8 Halogen suffix
9 Clothing supporter
10 Just about
11 Goof off
12 Lumberjack's tool
13 ___-do-well
21 Playthings
23 Scottish inventor James
25 Takes home
26 Potato alternative
27 *Otello*, e.g.
28 Breathes out loud
29 *"10"* star Bo
30 Eschew the restaurant
31 Fleet-footed
32 Bike with a small engine
34 "Uncle Miltie"
37 Cruise
38 "Cut it out!"
40 Eye problem
41 Whipping boy
43 Fed notes
44 Phone receiver's spot
46 Make a profit of
47 The Fatman's partner
48 ___ Mountains (continent-separating range)
49 Carefree adventure
50 Made tracks
51 Scottish isle
52 "You ___?" (butler's line)
53 Former mates
56 Actress Lupino

113 AROUND THE BANK

ACROSS

1 Certain bank, and the theme of this puzzle
6 Pastel shade
10 Talk trash to
14 Mount of the Ten Commandments
15 Go against
16 First name in jazz
17 Gladiator's locale
18 Cold-cut store
19 Hit the ground
20 "Peanuts" theme song
23 Hot tub
26 Save, with "away"
27 Less polite
28 Book by Bellow
30 Losers, in a taunt
32 Guitarist Eddie Van ___
33 Porter's regretful miss
35 D.H. Lawrence novel
41 Pain in the neck
42 Feels pain
44 Van Buren's twin sister
49 Usually welcome smack
50 Sky blue
51 "Later!"
53 Swine's confines
54 Traditional Jewish nosh
58 First name in gymnastics

59 Captain Picard's counselor
60 Big name in catalogs, once
64 Army surgeon Walter
65 Knowledgeable about
66 Part of a big name in Chinese history
67 Admission exams
68 Sonnet or haiku
69 Allots, with "out"

DOWN

1 Fed. benefit source
2 Televise
3 U-turn from SSW
4 Pioneer Boone, commonly
5 Glenn Close's Dangerous ___
6 American Idol judge Paula
7 Search for the Holy Grail, e.g.
8 Where John Wooden coached
9 Related
10 Close tightly
11 Make reference
12 One who hits to the side
13 Woodland deities
21 Harp at
22 Dr. of rap
23 "Quiet down!"

24 Little green edibles
25 He sang about Alice
29 ___ and the Art of Motorcycle Maintenance
30 Lose freshness
31 Paul Anka's "___ Beso"
33 Change for a five
34 QB successes
36 4, in some dates
37 Split
38 Environmental prefix
39 Greek consonants
40 The Anabaptists, e.g.
43 Retiring
44 Plugs away
45 Type of rhododendron
46 Gold piece
47 Is apprehensive of
48 Snaky fish
49 My gal, in song
51 Hundred-dollar bill
52 Particular dialect
55 "Cool it!"
56 Satirical cartoonist Peter
57 Prefix with phobia
61 Part of APB
62 Charlotte of Bananas
63 ___-boom-bah

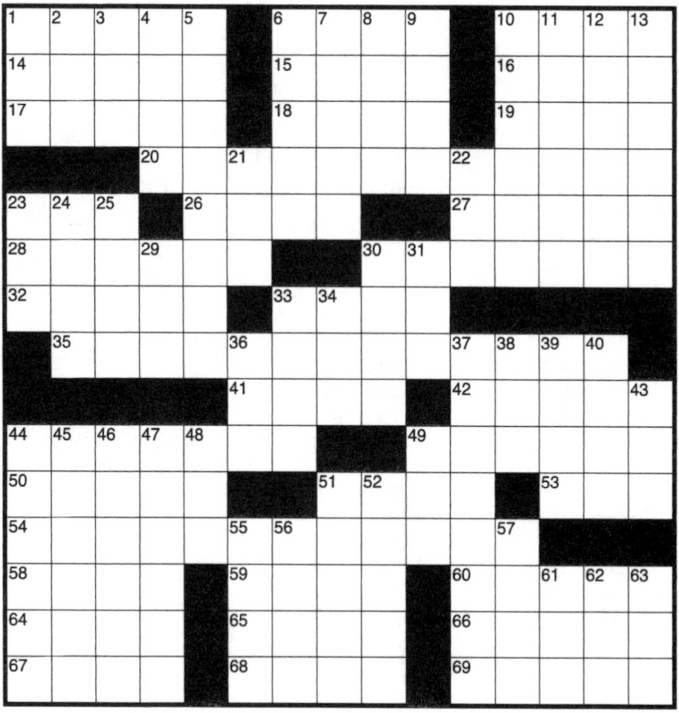

114 HAPPY FATHER'S DAY

ACROSS

1 Use cross hairs
4 Pitcher's stat
7 Silver and gold
13 Coated, like fish sticks
15 Throws in the towel
16 City on the Tigris River
17 Statue of Liberty's home
18 Have at
19 West Indies isle
20 Sell up the river
22 Vane dir.
23 Nautilus habitat
26 The feminine side
27 Harper Valley org.
30 Linda, of the sitcom *Alice*
33 "Scram!"
38 Ultimate example
40 To the second power
41 "Doggone!"
43 Confining, with "down"
44 Nasal consonants
45 Brit word book
47 Suffer the consequences
48 Drink little by little
51 Maps within maps
54 Lobster look-alikes

58 Unfounded fear
62 Kiev's republic
63 Thingamajigs
64 Lures
65 Golda Meir, for one
66 Stick, but not a twig
67 Pig's digs
68 Sports "noncombatant"

DOWN

1 Quatrain rhyme scheme
2 Levin and Gershwin
3 Ryan and Tilly
4 Aviator Rickenbacker
5 Land and buildings
6 Do sum math
7 Actress Rogers
8 Like a deadlocked score
9 Lois, in *Lois & Clark*
10 Remark to the audience
11 *Star Wars* director
12 Big pip on one ace
14 He wounded a white whale
15 Player of golf
19 Fish habitat
21 Gotten out of the bed

23 Vehicle with runners
24 Honoree of this puzzle
25 Enthusiastic
27 Rapidly, briefly
28 Tightly stretched
29 Forever's partner
31 "Let ___"
32 Name of a thing
34 Rob of *Melrose Place*
35 Coffee grinder setting
36 Horne of plenty of music
37 High-strung
39 Wife's title
42 Charged particles
46 Remove from the throne
48 Diver's gear
49 Ticked off
50 Toast lightly
51 Midmonth date
52 Sticker on a rose
53 Bubbly beverage
55 Bubbles behind a boat
56 Christian with style
57 Archer without arrows?
59 Max of *The Beverly Hillbillies*
60 Out of work
61 "Yeah, sure!"
63 Guacamole or fondue

115 THAT'S ALL SHE WROTE

ACROSS

1 Lose one's footing
5 Hangs in there
10 Words with shame or boy
14 El ___, Texas
15 Pueblo home
16 Big top barker
17 Above a lengthy corridor?
20 Football supporter
21 Home of Disney World
22 Give in to gravity
23 Test for size
25 Poet's before
26 Doofus
28 Cry of frustration
30 Surefire winner
31 Bk. of the Pentateuch
32 Syrian leader
36 Basilica section
37 Holy shroud?
40 Year-___-glance
43 Fanciful
44 "Don't mind ___ do"
47 Ramadan or January
49 Sporty Pontiac of yore

50 ___ sanctum
52 Houston nine
54 Wesley of *Blade*
55 Nervy French leader?
59 Not outstanding
60 Witty Woody
61 Sidewalk eatery
63 Fashion magazine
64 Cobblers' products
65 Screen symbol
66 Use a blowtorch
67 Blackjack request
68 Dork

DOWN

1 Caught sight of
2 Role of Penny's
3 Words to a toddler
4 ___ favor
5 Cowardly Lion portrayer Bert
6 Dance partner of Fred
7 Type of flare or panel
8 Steakhouse offering
9 Put in the mail
10 "Sort of" suffix
11 Coffeehouse alternative

12 Antipasto meats
13 Completely consumed
18 Chinese society
19 "Gee whillikers!"
24 Triple play trio
27 Stoker's supply
29 Greeting to the Chief
30 Mt. Rushmore's state
33 Tucked in
34 Proofreader's mark
35 Lhasa ___
38 Can't stomach
39 Telling tales
40 Famous jour. publisher
41 Proportionately
42 Insect colony
44 One way to jog
45 Empathize with
46 Its job is taxing
48 Bought and sold
51 Meat vitamin
53 Lower, as prices
54 Just know
56 K through 12
57 Piggy bank opening
58 Judge
59 Church bench
62 Dead or living follower

116 INFER THE ANSWERS

ACROSS

1 They reproduce without sex
8 Insectivorous creature
16 Ad infinitum
17 Freaking out
18 Where they say "What fer?"
20 Golfer Palmer, informally
21 Headlight protectors
22 North Pole saint
23 Helper of 22-Across
25 Consume entirely
28 Garfunkel and Linkletter
31 Skip past
33 Take-home amount
38 Do more than stretch the truth
39 Roth offerings
40 Sling mud at
41 Where they say "What fur?"
44 Clueless
45 Where to order a stack
46 67.5°
47 Rub the wrong way
48 Penetrate slowly
49 Time to beware
50 *Love Story* author Erich
52 Lay down the lawn
54 Series ender
58 Swit TV costar

60 Finish second
64 Where they say "What fir?"
68 Ability to stay calm
69 Seeks the office of
70 Golfer from South Africa
71 Hanging in the balance

DOWN

1 Concluding musical passage
2 ___ about (roughly)
3 Frequent chess sacrifice
4 Concave belly buttons
5 Henry Ford's son
6 Pal of Piglet
7 Give the cold shoulder to
8 Horrified
9 Radio static, e.g.
10 Type of ear
11 Pull the plug on
12 Feudin' with
13 Ride with a meter
14 Cast-of-thousands film
15 Stink to high heaven
19 Statement of the obvious
24 View in the crystal ball
26 Fixes, as a drain
27 Revive the spirits of

28 Site of many promises
29 Dogie catcher
30 LBJ, e.g.
32 *The War of the Worlds* invader
34 Turner of TV channels
35 Stuck one's nose in
36 In concert
37 Sycophant's answers
39 Megastars, to fans
40 *A Hard Road to Glory* author Arthur
42 Sort
43 Gives way
48 Bar food
49 Least busy
51 Egypt's Nasser
53 Starts doing business
54 Pilate's "Behold!"
55 Explorer Heyerdahl
56 Elvis ___ Presley
57 Taylor of *I Shot Andy Warhol*
59 Razor brand
61 Code word for A
62 Chuck wagon honcho
63 French I verb
65 "Thar ___ blows!"
66 Pebble Beach peg
67 Wheel track

198

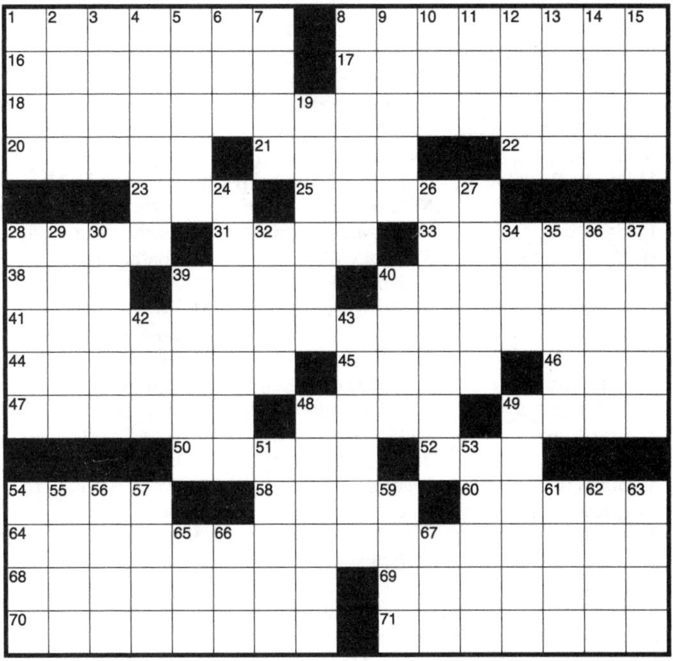

117 THE YEAR 2000

ACROSS

1 Data card debris
5 Word on an octagon
9 How easy it may be
14 Anise-flavored liqueur
15 Take on cargo
16 Volunteer's phrase
17 Marching band leader
19 Pushes through small holes
20 Steady flow
21 Flat sharer
23 Thin coin
25 Sci-fi flick about giant ants
26 One that beats all, in cards
29 Spill the beans
31 Very soon
35 Communion chalice
36 Winner of two Triple Crowns
38 Villain of *The Lion King*
39 Big name in vermouth
41 Pub offering
42 It may have a blade
43 Transactional analysis phrase
44 Full of peaks
46 Bit of a bite
47 D of A.D.
49 Engages in hostilities
50 Alternative to HBO

51 "A ___ gotta do what a ..."
53 Accommodating night owls
55 Shoe store name
59 Six-time N.L. home run champ
63 Like *The X-Files*
64 Creator of movies
66 Nose job?
67 Nobel Peace Prize winner Wiesel
68 U.S. Supreme Court count
69 Soft to the touch
70 Carson's Carnac, for one
71 Word with top or calendar

DOWN

1 Atlantic swimmers
2 Sidelined with injuries
3 France's Côte d'___
4 Like a rotunda
5 Prison, in slang
6 Muslim cap
7 What the nose knows
8 Presidential candidate Ross
9 Guys in the skies
10 Diver's face protector
11 Elite alternative
12 "Why should ___ you?"
13 Additional
18 Rum cocktail

22 John Glenn's home state
24 Dana of *The Sting*
26 Sharp-smelling
27 Former governor Mario
28 English derby town
30 Legal drama with Susan Dey
32 Meager
33 Have pizza delivered, say
34 Inched
37 Similar to a sovereign
40 Low-fat beverage
42 Word with solar or nervous
44 Mil. role for the president
45 Frasier portrayer Kelsey
48 To wit
52 Boxes for valuables
54 African antelope
55 Dick Tracy's girlfriend Trueheart
56 Starter meaning "half"
57 First name in pitching
58 River of the Pharaohs
60 *The Grapes of Wrath* extra
61 Change for a hundred
62 *Star ___: The Next Generation*
65 Tell a whopper

118 AN I FOR AN EYE

ACROSS

1 Yang's counterpart
4 Birdie on a par-three hole
7 Adopted boy, perhaps
14 Loss of loam
16 Female lead in a story
17 Layered pasta
18 Stirred up
19 I doctor?
21 Rock music's Jethro ___
22 Pop singer from Nigeria
26 Least cooked
30 Thompson of *Sense and Sensibility*
34 Strong coffee, in slang
35 Molecule member
36 Rapid I movement?
38 Spruce, e.g.
41 Sidewise, as a glance
42 Private I?
44 Skyrocket
45 A. York, for one
46 Expressed, as a farewell
47 Has a hankering
49 Rowlands of *Gloria*
51 Engraving tools
53 I shadow?
61 Between a rock and a hard place
64 Surrounded by
65 Lay down
66 Sprig on a plate
67 Tell the story of
68 Blasting material
69 Long beginning

DOWN

1 Shrill cry
2 Retirement accts.
3 Prone to snoop
4 Dancer's garment
5 Was victorious
6 ___ fours
7 Uneven hairdo
8 Polo of *Beyond Borders*
9 Passionate love
10 Sticks out the lips
11 Spanish affirmatives
12 Smallest bill
13 Beatty of *Roseanne*
15 Missile defense org.
20 Toast topper
23 Key with no sharps or flats
24 Sandy of *The Hogan Family*
25 Sidewalk trimmers
26 Driving cars competitively
27 "Yesterday!"
28 Chinese dumpling
29 Islamic leader
31 Ring around the castle
32 Hosp. honchos
33 Put the question to
36 He had a horse voice
37 "That ___ close one!"
39 Watch chain
40 Braun or Perón
43 Make over
47 He will agree
48 Companion for protection
50 Merchant John Jacob
52 Unfitting
54 Bear up there
55 Borscht need
56 Sign over
57 HMO offering
58 Stare at
59 Computer operator
60 Ophthalmo-logical problem
61 Grecian vase of verse
62 Small shooter pellet
63 All Fools' Day mo.

119 NOBLESSE OBESE

ACROSS
1 Servings of suds
6 Mabley of comedy
10 "Beat it!"
15 Poe's talking bird
16 Sitcom actor Thicke
17 Clinton Cabinet member
18 Land
20 Footnote abbr.
21 Silent film comic actor Roscoe
23 Bitter outburst
26 Collection of records for computer processing
27 Manipulative type
28 Tenant's payment
32 Ending with peace or beat
33 Nixon's pal Rebozo
34 Harden
36 Cozy places
40 Event where one may spell "hymenopteran"
41 "That's all, folks!" speaker
43 Saigon's site, for short
44 1945 conference site
46 Neighbor of Saudi Arabia
47 Long skirt
48 Meas. of time
50 Insect repellent brand
51 "Just for the heck ___"

52 Runs in the altogether
56 Attack like a sniper
58 "Let's Twist Again" singer
62 Kidney-related
63 Shout in a Handel chorus
67 Baked-brick building
68 Lapel device
69 Skate's bottom
70 Window divisions
71 Nabisco nosh
72 Historical figure of fable

DOWN
1 Word said while shivering
2 Arctic explorer John
3 Zsa Zsa's sister
4 Part of HEW
5 "Slammin' Sammy" of the links
6 *Today* cohost Lauer
7 Word on a lotion bottle
8 ___ Hari
9 Bergen was his "spokesman"
10 Looking for new talent
11 Sweet treat in paper
12 Coolers of drinks
13 Miss by ___
14 Sacred song
19 Mono counterpart

22 Embargo
23 With 39-Down, Kentucky basketball coach
24 "___ bad moon rising ..."
25 One without a cause, in cinema
29 "Just you wait, ___ 'iggins!"
30 Heated in the microwave
31 "I'm all ears"
35 It has a duel purpose
37 Confused condition
38 Moves down the runway
39 See 23-Down
41 Allegorical stories
42 Outflow's opposite
45 Movie about Ruth
47 Anarchy
49 It's vanilla in a Tom Cruise flick
52 Quarrel
53 Silents star Bara
54 Go without interruption
55 Witless one
57 Peach ___
59 Narrow margin
60 Sommer in the movies
61 Role for Liz
64 New Testament bk.
65 Bother, in a title of the bard
66 In the know

1	2	3	4	5		6	7	8	9		10	11	12	13	14
15						16					17				
18				19							20				
		21							22						
23	24	25						26							
27				28	29	30	31		32						
33				34			35		36		37	38	39		
40			41					42		43					
44		45		46					47						
		48	49		50				51						
52	53	54		55			56	57							
58					59	60	61								
62				63						64	65	66			
67				68				69							
70				71				72							

120 THE WEDDING SINGERS

ACROSS

1 Facts
5 Beginning for photo
9 Lemon-flavored, maybe
14 Like a turned ear
15 The yoke's on them
16 *Seven Samurai* director Kurosawa
17 Like the air that things disappear into
18 Italian auto
19 Kind of beer
20 He sang "The Wedding Song"
23 "I've been ___!"
24 Zest
25 Ledger column
27 He sang "Hawaiian Wedding Song"
32 'Zine
35 Allied commander of 1918
36 Buster Brown's dog
37 ___ Z
38 Worry
42 Partner of games
43 Keyboard instrument
45 Silver suffix
46 Halves of ems
47 He sang "The Hawaiian Wedding Song"

52 Cause of chaotic weather
53 Sheriff's band
57 WWII zone
58 He sang "Wedding Song (There Is Love)"
62 Beverage cart locale
64 Old fruit drink
65 Warty hopper
66 Dirty political tactic
67 Profit
68 Spy Mata ___
69 Contract conditions
70 Poet St. Vincent Millay
71 Word that may follow anything

DOWN

1 Label reading "Hello, my name is ..."
2 Kind of jacket
3 Doesn't pass
4 Worth mentioning
5 Bean curd
6 Red letters over a door
7 Levi's mother
8 Lure into crime
9 *Thy Neighbor's Wife* author Gay
10 Police file letters
11 Nocturnal entertainment

12 Lubricant pump
13 Play area
21 Plays on fairways
22 Medit. land
26 Superlative ending
28 "I do," e.g.
29 Frozen dessert
30 Head and shoulders protection
31 Deep desires
32 Papa's mate
33 Formerly or simultaneously
34 One gracious in defeat
39 Mai ___ cocktail
40 *The Stepford Wives* author Levin
41 Musician's speed
44 MD for women
48 Windshield musts
49 Pig ___ poke
50 Type of chair or wear
51 Calm down
54 "Here's to you!"
55 Scorches
56 Singer Gorme
57 Right on the map
59 Show the way
60 Knee neighbor
61 Rocker Turner
63 On the ___

121 EXPLODING FIREWORKS

ACROSS

1 Air resistance
5 Most prudent
11 Twice-chewed food
14 Cry of despair
15 Cleopatra's tragic lover
16 Lending letters
17 Up-to-date ditch?
19 Charlotte of *The Facts of Life*
20 Family car
21 Fencing moves
23 Esau's brother
26 College treasurers
27 Greenspan of interest
28 Homer-hitter Roger
31 Away from the wind
32 Finish first
33 Pyle, of the USMC on TV
34 *Unsafe at Any Speed* author
35 Step for regular people?
38 Dancing Fred's sister
40 Kinshasa's country
41 Lady's cry of exasperation
44 Melville's Billy
45 Battle of the ___
46 "Don't let that golf ball hit ya!"
47 Turns to water again

49 Desi of *I Love Lucy*
50 One who idolizes
51 *The ___ Kid* ('50s Western)
54 Patriotic women's org.
55 Place for lovers?
60 Airport monitor info
61 Take to the extreme
62 Frankenstein's lab assistant
63 "Runaway" singer Shannon
64 Color of cowards
65 Wild Bill

DOWN

1 DeLuise of comedies
2 R in Greek
3 To boot
4 Enters the stage
5 Magician's stick
6 Peruvian pyramid builder
7 "The Man" Musial
8 Time spent on hold, seemingly
9 Badly confused predicaments
10 T of MTM
11 Tempter of the flesh?
12 In trouble
13 Vanity that may reflect on you
18 One of Lee's men
22 Sci-fi's Asimov

23 Gossip
24 Cassius Clay, today
25 Stock point of a fable?
26 Teller of secrets, in a saying
28 Pop's partner
29 Blows away
30 Take it easy
33 Test for U. seniors
34 Compass pt.
36 More advanced in years
37 MacLeish's "___ Poetica"
38 Rubbed the wrong way
39 Bill deadline
42 NOW-supported legislation
43 Pince-___ (type of glasses)
45 Worked hard
46 Play around
48 Jim Croce's "Bad, Bad ___ Brown"
49 Card with one pip
51 *Abraham Lincoln* author Sandburg
52 Front end of China
53 Flat-bottomed boat
56 Blanc of cartoon voices
57 Past
58 "Yes" gesture
59 Not sweet, in a wine cellar

122 SOUNDS OF THE PAST

ACROSS

1 Stand in need of
5 Leather band
10 Rock group from Sydney
14 Raison d'___
15 Furry Australian
16 Someone who acts
17 Comedian Wilson moaned?
19 Spray weapon
20 Tell mama
21 Expert abilities
23 S&L earning
24 Think the world of
28 On offense, in baseball
29 Cook with vapor
31 Burton of *Star Trek: The Next Generation*
33 Neighbor of Eng.
34 Shopping spot
35 Dug at no time?
37 Ref. room offering
39 Bond creator Fleming
40 Some music forbidden?
46 Jupiter and Saturn but not Mars
50 St. crosser
51 Yarn unit
52 Small part for a big name
53 Union general at Gettysburg
55 *The Marriage of Figaro,* for one

57 H.S. promoter
58 Dahl or Francis
60 To the back of the boat
62 Persia today
63 Urban area battled?
67 Penny
68 Humble house
69 Simpatico sounds
70 Totals up
71 Kicks out
72 Concerning

DOWN

1 Philosophy of southpaws?
2 Site of Six Flags Over Georgia
3 Animal friend
4 Continued, with "on"
5 Slid on slats over slush
6 Put on fine clothes, with "out"
7 Word from the bleachers
8 Stout, for example
9 Notebooks
10 Fess up
11 Coke container
12 Announce officially
13 Reached the highest point, as waves
18 Criticize harshly
22 Fate
25 "Stick that bull!"

26 MLK title
27 First bone transplant recipient?
30 Running the whole gamut
32 Without water
35 It separates Mont. from Minn.
36 Machu Picchu resident
38 Buddy of *The Beverly Hillbillies*
40 Montego Bay's island
41 Affirmed with confidence
42 New ___ (Australia neighbor)
43 Keanu Reeves's role in *The Matrix*
44 Pup's bite
45 Chemical suffix
47 Electrical units
48 Strategic withdrawal
49 What's-his-name
52 Hispanic house
54 Fender-bender damages
56 Singer Lou
59 Cave ricochet
61 Glen Campbell's "___ Little Kindness"
64 Promissory letters
65 Boob tubes
66 "Are we having fun ___?"

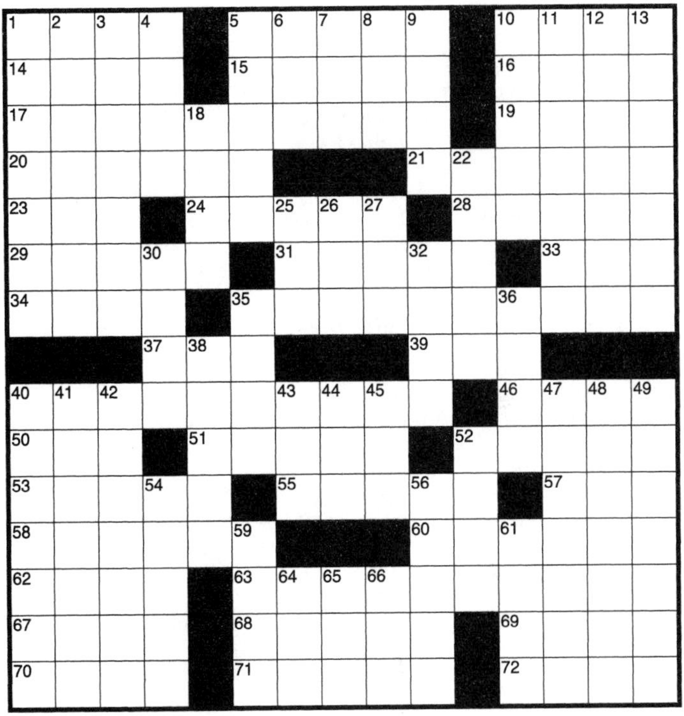

123 EXPRESS YOURSELF WITH CLOTHING

ACROSS
1 Responded to the alarm clock
5 Mailbag attachment
10 First lady Truman
14 Colored part of the eye
15 She may cry "Uncle"
16 "___, Brute?"
17 *The Opposite of Sex* star Kudrow
18 Discombobulate
19 Bangkok resident
20 Going bankrupt
23 Freddy Krueger's street
24 Buckeyes' sch.
25 City of Honshu
26 Ocean areas
28 Odes and such
32 ___ favor ("Please," to Pedro)
33 Brit. lexicon
35 Ins. letters
36 Name of twelve popes
37 Asking for contributions
41 Group of quail
42 What can start a -phyte?
43 ___ *Fine Day*
44 Road atlas abbr.
45 "My goodness!"
47 Live

51 Eliot's "cruellest month"
53 IBM's innards
55 Honolulu gift
56 Being boss
61 Toy building block
62 Name on a bomber
63 Santa checks it twice
64 Lacking bumps
65 Track transaction
66 *Bus Stop* playwright
67 Cincinnati team
68 Makes a switch
69 Roger Rabbit or Bugs Bunny

DOWN
1 Signed over, as an inheritance
2 Maryland's state bird
3 Request to Kate
4 Morales of *La Bamba*
5 Hose woes
6 Make neater
7 Make over
8 Scopes trial org.
9 Kind of group or pressure
10 "... hallowed ___ name ..."
11 Neighbor of Sudan

12 Begin
13 They who woo
21 Scents organs?
22 Wild blue yonder
27 Flower shop purchase
29 George Burns movie
30 911 call respondent
31 Manhattan neighborhood
34 Fender bender scar
36 "That was close!"
37 Personal bugbear
38 Did a mean job?
39 Pedagogic org.
40 Turn out to be
41 Tough guy
45 Samuel's mentor, in the Bible
46 Carry
48 Weather whipping boy
49 "C'mon!"
50 Lend an ear
52 Some of Tiger's tools
54 Bosc and Anjou
57 Front-page stuff
58 Nibble, beaver-style
59 Roman robe
60 Came to rest

212

FORE! CRYING OUT LOUD

ACROSS
1 Barks like a Chihuahua
5 Reloading need
9 Weakling, next to the pen
14 Lawman at the O.K. Corral
15 Pooh or Yogi
16 Sonja of *Thin Ice*
17 Fore! the record?
19 Lickety-split
20 Souped-up bike
21 Fore! fear?
23 Former secretary of state Dean
26 Diamonds, in slang
27 Raw metal
28 Top fighter pilots
29 Grand or upright
31 Automaker Ransom
32 Wrestling area
33 Monitor's beat
34 Parcel out
35 Fore! the best?
38 Entire range
41 Songwriter Bacharach
42 EMT's skill
45 During the course of
46 Word with rib or interest rate
48 Sensitive to pain
49 Caesar of *Your Show of Shows*
50 "Long," in Hawaiian

51 Jackets with open fronts
53 Fore! services rendered?
56 English coppers
57 More competent
58 Fore! money?
61 West Point newbie
62 Bring home the bacon
63 Began golfing, with "off"
64 Splinter groups
65 Like Easter eggs
66 Racetrack info

DOWN
1 Respectful affirmative
2 Former Chrysler head Lee
3 Isaiah or Jeremiah
4 Binges
5 Start of a kindergarten song
6 Confession starter
7 Fourth rock from the Sun
8 Confer ministerial office on
9 Window treatment
10 Turned on the waterworks
11 In the zone
12 Lucy's last name on *I Love Lucy*

13 Most profound
18 Asner and Ames
22 Cpl., for one
24 October birthstone
25 River near the Great Pyramid
30 Cover story
31 Good ___ boy
33 Right out of the oven
34 Picnic crasher
35 Patricia Neal's Best Actress film
36 Ready for the dentist's drill
37 Sweet sandwich
38 Lids for fuel tanks
39 Good-natured
40 Center of the keyboard
42 Like those who nibble around the ears?
43 Go ahead
44 Plants again, as a lawn
46 Luau paste
47 Wandered
48 Takes care of
50 Greek stringed instruments
52 Hosp. staffer
54 Borrower's burden
55 Confederate uniform color
59 Before
60 What this clue is, with "the"

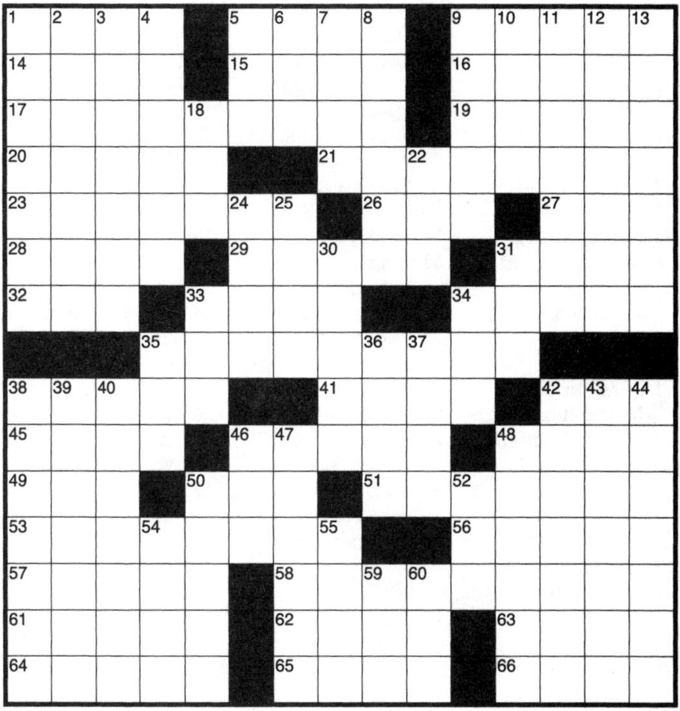
1
2
3
4
5
6
7
8
9
10
11
12
13
14
15
16
17
18
19
20
21
22
23
24
25
26
27
28
29
30
31
32
33
34
35
36
37
38
39
40
41
42
43
44
45
46
47
48
49
50
51
52
53
54
55
56
57
58
59
60
61
62
63
64
65
66

125 LETTER OPENERS

ACROSS

1 Cutting remark
5 Marching band instrument
10 Old gray animal of song
14 Cream-filled cookie
15 Blade holder
16 Length x width
17 Skill of Superman
19 Belgian river
20 Joked with
21 1961 Best Actor Maximilian
23 "Now ___ seen everything!"
24 Andretti or Allison
28 *Iceland* star
29 Linger
31 Riboflavin and others
33 Feline in a flick
34 Tooth straighteners
35 Like a system of scientific meas.
36 *Gone With the Wind* plantation
38 Actors that overdo it
40 Bk. before James
43 Bother or burrowing animal
45 Basics of a subject

49 Series about a Roman emperor
51 Tied at a point apiece
52 Guided trips
53 Available from the keg
55 Bit of caroling
56 Public outbursts
58 Gridiron ball-carrier
60 Put on the staff
61 Red meat choice
65 Tributes in verse
66 Specter of government
67 Perry Mason writer Gardner
68 Joins with rings
69 Persona non ___
70 Join by fusing

DOWN

1 Toy for windy days
2 Touchdown for the jets
3 Literate people
4 William of westerns
5 Film about Mexican painter Kahlo
6 "Viva ___ Vegas!"
7 Dangerous sprayer
8 When repeated, affected

9 Sea eagles
10 Rowdy disorder
11 Poison in classic mysteries
12 In a daze
13 Like harp seals
18 Part of VIP
22 Gaping fissure
25 Short-distance transmitter
26 NASA outing
27 Most fattening
30 No-goodnik
32 Dotted-line instruction
34 Pitt of *Troy*
37 Treat harshly
39 Word with Juan
40 Broadway success
41 Greenpeace concern
42 Purplish
44 Starter's need
46 "We're expecting you!"
47 Panacea
48 Gave off flashes
50 *Gunsmoke* star James
51 Work of art
54 Spot for sports
57 Doe's counterpart
59 Do a slow burn
62 Shiverer's utterance
63 Scandal suffix
64 Surfing site

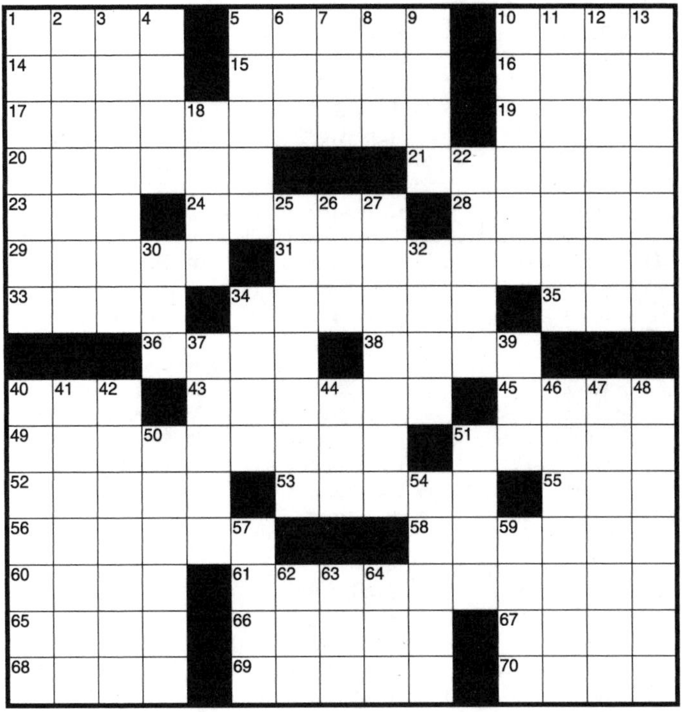

126 BUM STEERS

ACROSS

1 Org. founded on Lincoln's birthday
6 Cold war news name
10 Sandwich, in England
14 Come to pass
15 Pizarro foe
16 Carpet layer's calculation
17 World of sci-fi
18 Service period
19 Attire for Freddie the Freeloader
20 Amens?
23 Many a snake
24 It has a round cover
25 Insurance co. employee
26 Split
29 Hamlet and Ophelia, e.g.
30 Party big shot
32 Seasonal singer
35 Compulsive plastic users?
38 Worked in the stacks
39 In apple-pie order
42 Bring down

45 Falco of *The Sopranos*
47 Ruby, for one
48 They may be mixed at a court
51 Save
53 Hood from Chicago?
56 Turned on by
57 Publisher Henry
58 Brown and more
60 Need a bath badly
61 Maine, to Monet
62 Mini rhubarb
63 Ages and ages
64 Half a '50s sitcom couple
65 TV landlady of 64-Across

DOWN

1 "Fooled you!"
2 Like some hands
3 Puzzle type
4 Weightlifting set
5 Grace, e.g.
6 Marshal of southern Europe
7 Over
8 Take a hike
9 Ballroom activity
10 Driver from Kannapolis
11 Catherine's place

12 Fete
13 Burns misses
21 Stable scene
22 Sedated
23 Hem's partner
27 Compound in a shaker
28 Steered, or deal in steers
31 They may show signs of withdrawal
33 Had to pay
34 Door sign
36 Clam's home
37 Stand up for
40 Empty
41 So far
42 Look up to
43 Malay Archipelago island
44 Jane who wrote of Elinor
46 Certain duty
49 Fished for congers
50 Cook with an accent?
52 Violate the Tenth Commandment
54 Some VCRs
55 Mountain myth
59 Scale part

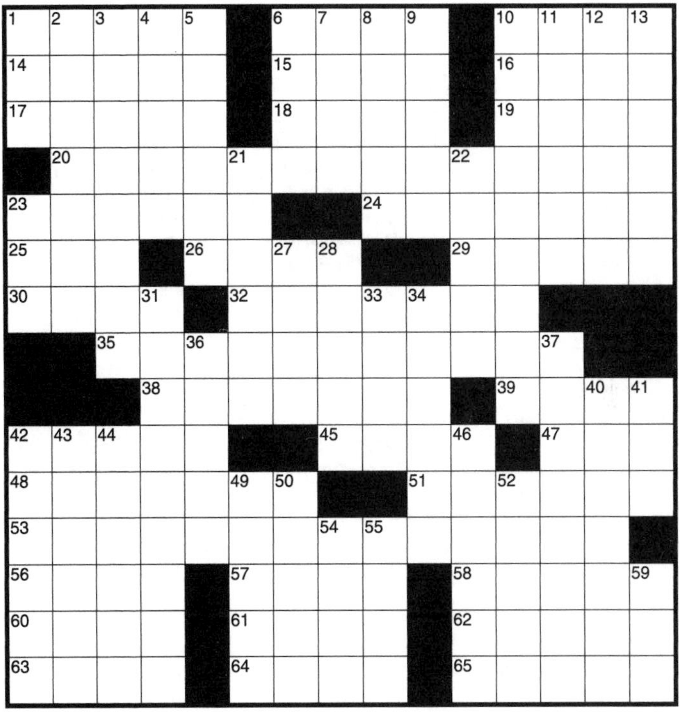

127 VOICE VOTE

ACROSS
1 Has at
8 Settle, with "of"
15 *Ben-Hur* vehicle
16 In writing
17 EYE
19 Long E in Greek
20 Kristofferson of *A Star Is Born*
21 Cirrocumulus clouds, e.g.
22 Insignificant individual
24 Play, for short
25 Result, as of a rocket launch?
28 Like tea in summer
30 Gore and Sharpton
33 Shankar's lute
34 Whoopi's *Sister Act* cover
35 Fill forcefully
36 NEIGH
40 Jamaican liquors
41 Speed limit letters
42 Title character in *The Little Mermaid*
43 Calendar abbr.
44 French Riviera town
45 Most offensive
46 Posed, perhaps
47 Safari superior

49 Gp. for songwriters
52 Seeks damages
53 Actress Zadora
56 ABS TENSION
60 Former inmate
61 Stuffed pasta
62 Boiling mad
63 "Dum-de-dum-dum" drama

DOWN
1 Dull pain
2 Open-and-___ case
3 Gilbert of *Roseanne*
4 Airport screen abbr.
5 Super Bowl that the Jets won
6 Necklace attachment
7 Belle or Bart
8 Prancer's aunts
9 Business trigram
10 Gushed out
11 Type of button
12 Withdraws, with "out"
13 Leak
14 Goes astray
18 Quash immediately
22 Siamese citizens, today
23 Threadbare
24 Descartes of math

25 They employ things
26 Arouse
27 Former tree
29 Putdown
30 *L.A. Law* lawyer
31 Adds alcohol to
32 Liquefy to refine
35 Server of beers on *Cheers*
37 Give off
38 Set of parallel bars, initially
39 Main Spanish plain precipitation
44 Hot jelly
45 Matthew of women's education
46 Navigator Islands, today
48 ___ Harold of Cosby cartoons
49 *Raiders of the Lost Ark* menaces
50 Intern's "Now!"
51 Apple refuse
52 Outbuilding
53 Laborer
54 Wight or Man
55 "Be that ___ may ..."
57 Bee chaser
58 Org. that gives a dam
59 Fix, as an election

1	2	3	4	5	6	7		8	9	10	11	12	13	14
15								16						
17							18							
19					20					21				
		22	23					24						
25	26	27					28	29				30	31	32
33						34				35				
36				37	38				39					
40				41						42				
43				44				45						
		46				47	48							
49	50	51			52					53	54	55		
56				57				58	59					
60							61							
62							63							

221

128 MY ACCESS CODE GOT PINCHED

ACROSS
1 Sentry's warning
5 Is in session
9 Tennis ball rotation
14 *A Death in the Family* author James
15 Comic strip dog
16 Vermont's Allen
17 To the north of some European mountains
19 It may be white
20 Trees with cones
21 Tiny Tim's instrument
22 Fixed pumps, maybe
24 Reserve
27 Leslie Caron title role
28 Give the ax to
29 Shelter for shooters
33 Nut with a cap
36 Count with a beat
37 Pub servings
38 On one's back
39 Gardner's lawyer
40 Country star McEntire
41 Prefix for angle or pod
42 Black on the screen
43 No medalist

44 Better than average
46 Home office site, maybe
47 Carpenter's fastener
48 Runner in the raw
53 Lofty peaks
56 Room opener
57 Heston's org.
58 The whole shebang
59 Sewing accessories
62 ___ a customer
63 Mimics
64 Enter quietly
65 Passover dinner
66 Kenny Rogers hit
67 Something to break or shake

DOWN
1 Bonnet securers
2 Be in harmony
3 Minimum amount
4 Half score
5 Penetrate
6 Ran without moving
7 Easy two-pointer
8 Student of palms
9 Kind of strength
10 Peter of *Becket*
11 Land of Manila
12 Letter enc.
13 Defeated at wrestling

18 Sarandon of *Shall We Dance*
23 Puckish
25 Plot piece
26 They get the lead out
30 Has the stage
31 The Everly Brothers' "Let ___ Me"
32 Former Russian ruler
33 Whodunit hound
34 Parking place
35 Dogmatic
36 Silents vamp Theda
39 Kind of sugar
40 First name in gossip
42 *Lake Wobegon Days* writer
43 Hanger-on
45 Leave the premises
46 Like garb for a gala
49 Brought into alignment
50 Small hill
51 Els with tees
52 Hoarse
53 Ford models
54 Zilch
55 Kind of column
60 1040 pro
61 Part of a Stein line

129 YOU ARE WHAT YOU EAT

ACROSS

1 Vigoda and Fortas
5 Plunk (down)
8 Share billing with another
14 Free
16 *Lawrence of Arabia* actor
17 Hook's foe
18 Small wave
19 Quick-bread-eating hunks?
21 Your physical self, for short
22 Labor Day's mo.
23 Gives approval to
24 Sunbathers catch these
25 Capp and Capone
28 Shade
29 Ballpoint, for one
30 Legislator
34 Angora fabric
37 Item of men's jewelry
38 City in *Gone With the Wind*
39 The ___ Trail
40 Return to the previous owner
41 Spot for the first shot
42 Sweet potato
43 ___ *Done Him Wrong*
44 Town, lake, or canal
46 Costello of comedy
47 Bro's sibling

50 *To Kill a Mockingbird* author Harper
51 Starchy-veggie-eating TV-watcher?
56 Made charts of
58 Increased in temperature
59 Baltimore ballplayer
60 Star on a Christmas tree, e.g.
61 Notices fragrances
62 Distress signal
63 Matches, as with a bet

DOWN

1 Swiss mounts
2 Sugar source
3 Ironically piercing rebuke
4 Eskimo transports
5 Kind of menu
6 Colorado Springs initials
7 Trucker's approval
8 De agony of de feet?
9 Elevator pioneer Elisha
10 Dip in gravy, as a biscuit
11 Fruit-eating bosses?
12 Metal mixture
13 Orchestra section
15 "It's either you ___"

20 Dick was his veep
24 Treatment program, for short
25 Low-voiced lady
26 Animal den
27 Dessert-eating beloved one?
28 Like cats that are with it
29 Northernmost or southernmost point
31 Fibber or Molly
32 Face saver?
33 Family
34 Channel with videos
35 Want to scratch
36 Leaf-moving tool
38 Point a slingshot, e.g.
40 South American cowboys
42 Thou, in modern speech
44 St. ___ Fire
45 Give guns to again
46 Veins without blood
47 Stretches across
48 Itsy-bitsy piece
49 Watch winders
51 Cooler room
52 Big sandwich
53 "Zip-___-Doo-Dah"
54 Pitch properly
55 Chooses, with "for"
57 Government wheeler-dealer

130 A CHANGE OF CLOTHING

ACROSS

1 New York nine
5 Companion of peck, in typing
9 Silky material
14 Seawater hue
15 Follow, as orders
16 In isolation
17 Moon goddess
18 *Laugh-In* line
20 Deadlock remedy
22 Carte start
23 Terminate
24 Domino of "Ain't That a Shame" fame
25 Printing mistakes
28 Ear stimulator
30 Name in the front of this book
31 Former Montreal player
32 Watergate judge
37 Clairvoyance, for example
38 Tips on rough water
41 Section of a circle
44 Phrase after well
45 Attention-getting sound
49 Gave a job to
51 Indy 500 vehicle
52 Black suit
54 Have the blahs

57 Become riper
58 Onetime terminal letters
59 Family insignia
62 Reel little bits
64 Robert E. and his kin
65 Parting word
66 Ammunition in slapstick comedy
67 Sand hill
68 Heavy, or intellectually lightweight
69 Kind of loser
70 Selects, with "for"

DOWN

1 Like a falcon of film
2 Time when day and night are equal
3 Got purring, in a way
4 Sporty car
5 Old Testament prophet
6 WWI attacker
7 Head supporters
8 Small child
9 Used chairs?
10 Places where "I do" is said
11 Past the deadline
12 Pen pals?

13 Bridal bio word
19 Strong emotion
21 *Mayberry* ___
26 Gather what you sow
27 Nile biter
29 Right this minute
32 Theology topic
33 Suffix for Israel
34 Give gas to
35 Hard water?
36 Passenger vehicle
39 Get out of sight
40 Sweat shop?
41 Sounds of relief
42 Current against the current
43 Enter on all fours
46 Gather with difficulty
47 Portion
48 Locks without keys
50 "My Cup Runneth Over" singer
51 Sports official
53 Univ. or coll.
54 Cuomo or Puzo
55 Aquatic mammal
56 Deputized dudes
60 Cry of the clumsy
61 Italian statesman Moro
62 Passing trend
63 Take to court

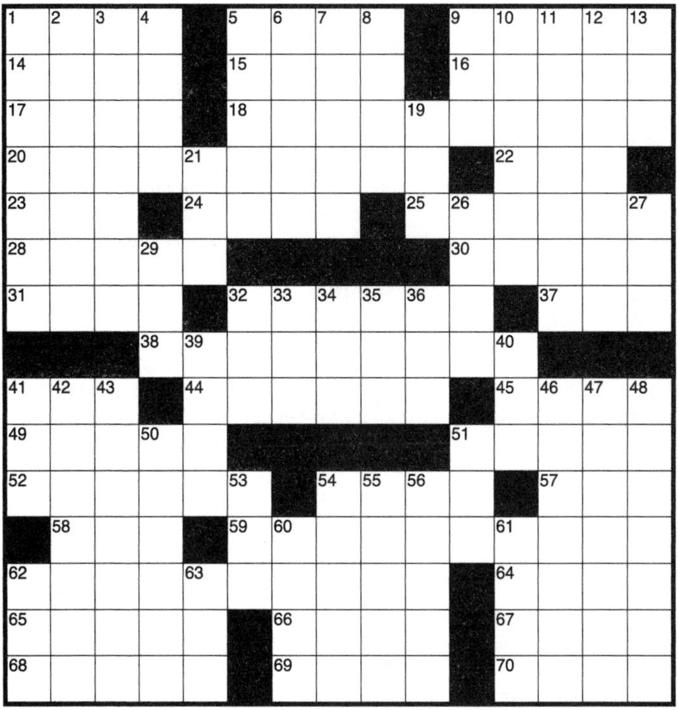

131 ABOUT MY HMO ...

ACROSS

1 Goulash, for example
5 German sub
10 Bygone leader
14 Duct drop
15 Jessica of *Driving Miss Daisy*
16 Words of woe
17 Strong inclination
18 Some singers
19 Off one's rocker
20 Protectorate of North Africa
23 Light drama
24 Elizabeth of *La Bamba*
25 Atlantic City attraction, with "the"
28 Emcee, e.g.
31 Role-reversing Hawkins
33 "It's c-c-c-cold!"
36 It drapes trees in the South
40 Votes in favor
42 Sharp as tacks
43 Puncturing tools
44 Woman at Woodstock, perhaps
47 Maiden name preceder
48 French farewell
49 Barely managed, with "out"
51 Stimpy's cartoon pal
52 Main point
56 Vital carrier
60 Cannons in a ditch
64 Least bit of concern
66 Marie Antoinette's husband
67 JFK postings
68 Merlin, e.g.
69 Celestial being
70 Margarita flavoring
71 Oklahoma tribe
72 Simple kind of question
73 Like some causes

DOWN

1 Cram full
2 Latin land
3 Gung-ho
4 Tool for twisting
5 Beach near Omaha
6 Soothing ointment
7 At the peak
8 Esteem to the extreme
9 Miss Jane Pittman portrayer Cicely
10 Bath powder
11 Debunk
12 Cable inits.
13 Vintage vehicle
21 Corporate VIPs
22 One way to pay
26 Way of the theater
27 Reverend Jackson
29 Meat in a can
30 Crunchy Tex-Mex snack
32 Doc's org.
33 Without printed music
34 Aptly named author
35 Champin' at the bit
37 Enthusiast, slangily
38 ___ *Jury* (Spillane novel)
39 Try to locate
41 Sault ___ Marie
45 Extremely successful
46 Area away from the battle
50 "I'm all ears!"
53 Dental filling
54 Baked breakfast item
55 Ruffians
57 Two to one, for one
58 Coal haulers
59 Plus in the ledgers
61 Short courses
62 Demeanor
63 Norwegian capital
64 It connects the words of four answers in this puzzle
65 Morsel for a mare

132 FISCALLY PHYSICAL

ACROSS
1 She sweeps on the job
5 War supporter
9 Going rate?
14 Like the fabled duckling
15 Queens stadium name
16 *Batman* police chief
17 Like most cagers
18 With 23-Across, fork over too much
20 Slugger's stat
22 Stem's opposite
23 See 18-Across
26 Be productive, in the coop
30 Fuel up
31 Pointed a finger at
33 Candy or sugar follower
34 Idaho city
35 Esteem highly
36 Underwrite
39 Black key above G
41 Fairy tale character
42 Former *Tonight Show* host Jack
43 Julia's role on *Seinfeld*
45 Buddy, in Bordeaux
48 Cut covering

50 With 55-Across, has an exorbitant price
52 Somber
54 Words of clarification
55 See 50-Across
60 "Take ___ your leader"
61 Rival of Florida State
62 Cleo's river
63 Zest for life
64 Correspond, grammatically
65 Bit of filming
66 Former netman Nastase

DOWN
1 Alter
2 Christie of mysteries
3 "Yeah, right!"
4 "Blowin' in the Wind" composer
5 Fortune
6 Nutty fruitcake center?
7 Kids' questions
8 Kind of drum
9 "Pardon me"
10 It might ring a bell
11 *La mer*, essentially
12 Small fraction of a joule
13 Long code sound

19 Pin part
21 In addition
24 Cat's eye, at times
25 Magi origin
27 Irk big-time
28 African plains grazer
29 Go out with
32 Bombay-born conductor
34 Chess, for one
35 Most despicable
36 Custard dessert
37 Rock's Clapton
38 Chastity, for one
39 Police alert, briefly
40 Airline watchdog org.
43 Mild epithet
44 Gershwin colleague Oscar
45 In addition
46 It may come with a small umbrella
47 Vocalize
49 *L.A. Law* lawyer
51 Oscar winner Marisa
53 Charles Lamb's pen name
55 G.P.'s gp.
56 Oil-drilling machinery
57 Ruin the appearance of
58 Lodge member
59 Thou

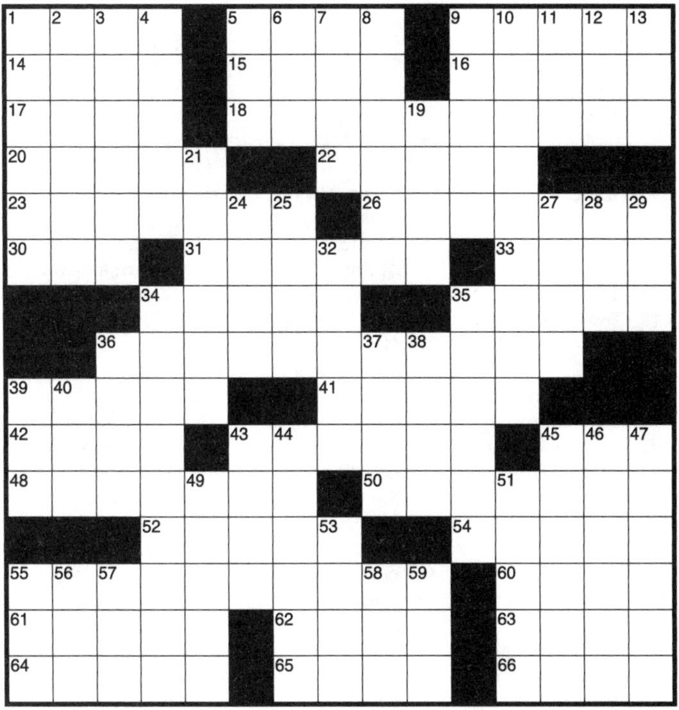

133 THE CALL OF THE DODO

ACROSS
1 Bro and sis
5 Type of bag
9 Gave from a deck
14 Mouth, in slang
15 *Gilmore Girls* daughter
16 Bother
17 Novelist Jaffe
18 "D'oh!"
20 Gray area?
22 Confess, with "up"
23 "___ been had!"
24 Prepare to hem
25 Fr. holy woman
26 LBJ or JFK
27 Do
30 Squirrel away
31 Indoor type of football
32 Pluto, for example
33 Ovine entreaty
36 In the main
38 Radical '60s org.
39 Starts
41 Ancient Celt
43 Make up (for)
44 Dough
48 Prefix with Tibetan
49 Paul Simon's "___ a Rock"
50 Winkler of *Happy Days*
51 Common article
52 Medium skill
53 Play with numbers

55 Doe
58 Fair-to-middling
59 Russian mountains
60 Ned Beatty's role in *Superman*
61 Temptation location
62 Sound at the end of day
63 Rowlands of *The Notebook*
64 Cranberry and cherry

DOWN
1 Handbag handles
2 Song by Alanis Morissette
3 Item on a monkey menu
4 Utensil for making flapjacks
5 Looking down
6 Looking up
7 Rainbow shape
8 One way to learn
9 Sunrise time
10 Vane dir.
11 Log holders
12 Like some vents
13 Prepares for the printer
19 Barnyard parent
21 Work on an organ, maybe
25 Celeb status

26 Bake sale sponsor, often
28 Role for Stack or Costner
29 "Leaving ___ Jet Plane"
30 Land vehicles without wheels
32 Put in a good word for
33 Willing to pat oneself on the back
34 Unlikely protagonist
35 In unison
37 Joe holder
40 Collaborator with Bowie
42 *An American Tragedy* writer
44 Compact canine
45 Translate from plaintext
46 Rubbed out
47 Hose not for the garden
49 Expert ending
52 Lanchester of *Bride of Frankenstein*
53 Word after chow
54 Major or Minor constellation
56 Barbary Coast country: Abbr.
57 Hot time in Le Havre

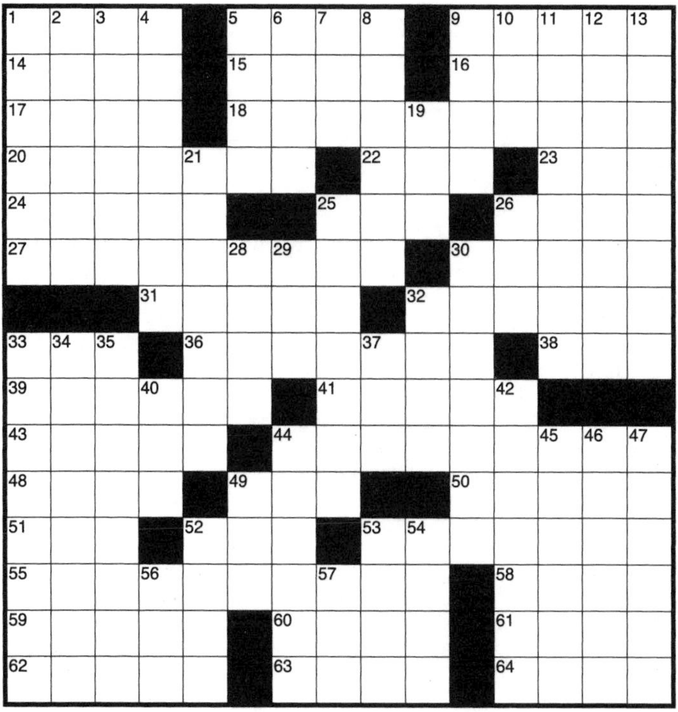

134 BARRELS OF FUN

ACROSS

1 Manger visitors
5 Greenish-blue
9 Wet behind the ears
14 Breezed through, as an exam
15 Iron coating, sometimes
16 Tended to a squeak
17 Use a rifle on trout?
19 Turns on the waterworks
20 Sonja of *Thin Ice*
21 Don King, to boxing
23 *Divine Comedy* author
25 Hawaiian island
26 Spray bullets under the hood?
32 Quick on the uptake
35 Hole in one's skin
36 Discarded, with "out"
37 He's a pig
39 ___ Domingo
42 Not so exciting
43 Hot, sweet beverage treat
45 Town known for winemaking?
47 "Well, ___ yer old man!"
48 Terrified toreador tactic?
52 Get the heck out of Dodge

53 *Ghostbusters* goo
56 Plant specialist
60 Endangered layer
62 Leslie of *An American in Paris*
63 What squirt guns do?
65 Barely moved
66 "Figwear" locale
67 Downey of *Touched by an Angel*
68 Hot sauce or hot music
69 Clarinetist's item
70 Prohibitionists

DOWN

1 Sitcom set in Korea
2 Felt hurt
3 She was Thelma in *Thelma & Louise*
4 Taking it easy
5 Lassie's warning
6 Witty words
7 Former rival of the U.S.
8 Not out
9 Good-for-nothing
10 Free of loopholes
11 "Would ___?"
12 Zig or zag
13 Marinaro and McMahon
18 Slacken

22 Investor's Fannie
24 Son of Seth
27 Singing syllable
28 Therefore
29 Nest eggs
30 Fictional sub captain
31 Woolly females
32 Initial course in elementary school?
33 Friend of Tigger and Eeyore
34 Tortilla and contents
38 Where good news is shouted
40 Notebook divider label
41 "Lord, have mercy ___"
44 Home of the Braves
46 Permit
49 X, on a sundial
50 Cow that's no mom
51 Gila monster, for one
54 Word with home or skills
55 The Riddler, to Batman
56 Theda ___
57 Pitcher Hershiser
58 Additional serving, as French fries
59 Trap on a limb
61 Pitcher stats
62 Syringe meas.
64 Purpose

234

135 CAN THEY CUT IT?

ACROSS

1 Army base
5 In flames
10 Social insect
14 In charge of
15 Weighted down
16 She performed with Duke
17 Hack
20 Blind one's response to healing
21 Battery size
22 Palindromic Gardner
23 Jousters will stick it to you
24 Small island
26 Forum garb
28 Jon Arbuckle's dog
29 Union demand
31 Merit badge locale
32 Stocking's end
33 Contented kitty's sound
34 Don of *Cocoon*
36 Hack
38 Spiff (up)
41 Long in the tooth
42 Pea container
45 Othello, ethnically
46 Decides not to solve or buy a vowel
48 Deal with it
49 Web-footed mammal
51 Commotion
52 Decorative vessels
53 City in Kirghizia
54 Busy mo. for the IRS
56 Use an easy chair
58 Hack
61 Wedding dance
62 *Frasier* dog
63 Smallest amount of change
64 Deer sir
65 Annoying kids
66 Bookmaker's numbers

DOWN

1 Cockpit companion
2 Alligator pear
3 Griffith of *Working Girl*
4 Charming, for one
5 "I cannot tell ___"
6 King or queen
7 Rhoda's mom
8 Races with batons
9 One-named Irish singer
10 Horror film director Craven
11 Poor Richard's book
12 Lacking originality
13 Flamboyant manner
18 "The Waste Land" author's monogram
19 Stop fasting
25 Attack from on high
27 Mouse manipulator
29 Goldberg and others
30 Locales for icicles
33 Lobbying org.
35 Pt. of MCAT
36 Restore to health
37 "Don't let that bother you"
38 Removes the wrinkles from
39 Random criticism
40 Financial planner's suggestion, maybe
42 Assumed as a fact
43 Allowing for future revision
44 They may be just
47 Strut like a peacock
48 Spotted, like some cats
50 "Far out!"
52 Taper of TV fare
55 Make ready for surgery
57 Flock females
59 Scrap of cloth
60 Sixes for the 49ers: Abbr.

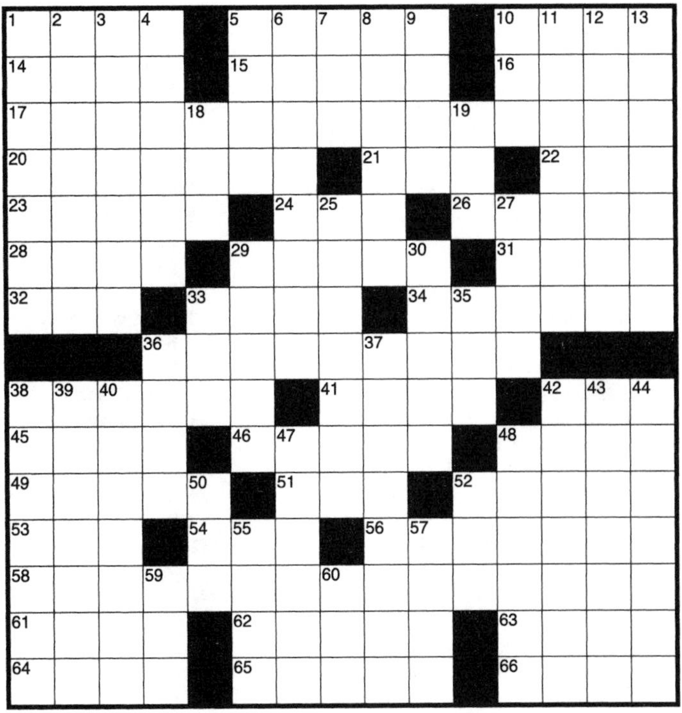
1 2 3 4 5 6 7 8 9 10 11 12 13
14 15 16
17 18 19
20 21 22
23 24 25 26 27
28 29 30 31
32 33 34 35
36 37
38 39 40 41 42 43 44
45 46 47 48
49 50 51 52
53 54 55 56 57
58 59 60
61 62 63
64 65 66

136 **PERSONALITY DISORDER**

ACROSS
1 Mafia boss
4 Sax mouthpiece
8 Went to the top of
14 Kind of
16 Dick Cheney's predecessor
17 Continent namesake
18 Relax
19 Fond of a garnish?
21 "Go ahead!"
22 A handful of
23 Art stand
28 Summer, in Paris
29 Cry like a kitty
30 Fictional reindeer feature
32 Cursive curlicue
34 Capitol figure
35 Stare open-mouthed
36 Shellfish without a pearl?
40 Brazilian soccer great
42 Mark before com
43 Bounty captain
46 At this point in time
48 Sounds of surprise
50 Gun lobby org.
51 1944 Philippines invasion site
52 Bancroft of *The Graduate*
54 Crystal ball gazer

55 Poet laureate?
58 "It's ___ all over again!"
62 Floppy
63 "Be right with you!"
64 Gives a name to
65 Publish alternative, on campus
66 Take ten
67 They have three ft.

DOWN
1 Gets the quotient
2 Monotonous
3 Less ethical trick?
4 Enlist anew
5 Pack up
6 Real estate account
7 Belief of Thomas Jefferson
8 Stuffing herb
9 Satiated
10 Tree rings' indication
11 End of a Hawaiian volcano
12 EMTs go to these
13 *L.A. Law* star Susan
15 Kiddie lit canine
20 Husband in the funny pages' "Lockhorns"

24 Christmas tree topper
25 Fly like Charlie Brown's kite?
26 Mind reader's gift
27 Gray general
29 U. degree for a painter
31 Ernie of the links
33 Start of a Tony Bennett title
34 It may call the kettle black
37 Altar assent
38 "In your dreams!"
39 Cable giant
40 Bosom buddy
41 Suffix with Japan
44 Said hello to
45 Take control of
47 Brain-body connectors
48 Part of AOL
49 Bank robberies
53 2000 presidential candidate
54 Leave in the text
56 "That smarts!"
57 Comedy sketch
58 Quick swim
59 U-turn from WSW
60 Canning container
61 "Just ___ thought!"

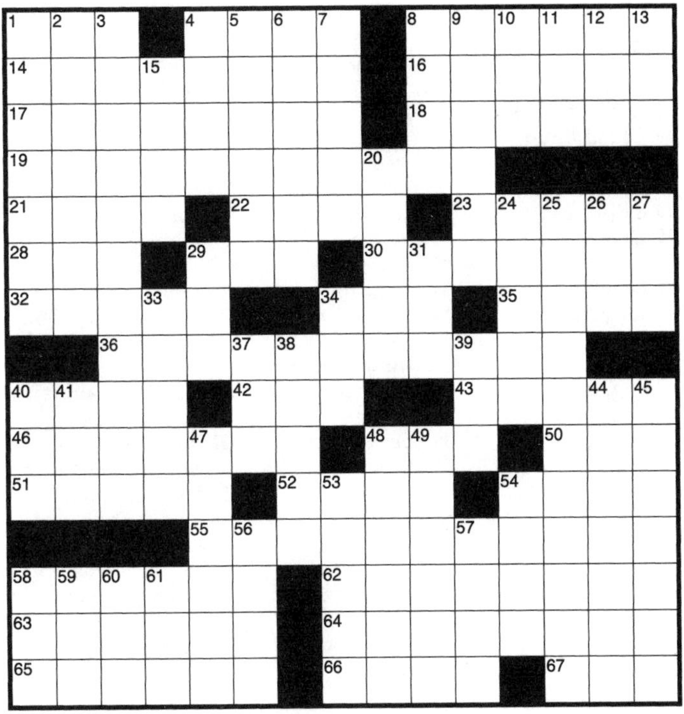

137 NET NOMENCLATURE

ACROSS

1 Depression-era org.
4 In short supply
10 Clamber up
14 Suffix with human or fact
15 Ship's shelter
16 Characteristic carrier
17 Scanning the Net for your name
19 Sharp to the taste
20 Jerusalem's country
21 Smart dresser
23 Same old same old
24 Go once over lightly
25 CEO's degree, perhaps
27 Davis of *Do the Right Thing*
29 60 secs.
30 Dazed state while waiting out a download
33 Part of the U.K.
34 Glinda portrayer in *The Wiz*
35 Sticks around
36 Pilaf ingredient
37 "... ___ is in heaven"
38 Semisoft Dutch cheese
40 Baldwin of *Prelude to a Kiss*
41 Coverage co.
44 Online enthusiast
46 Alley in a cave

47 Prefix with personal or planetary
48 Alternative to air conditioning
49 Symbol of stubbornness
50 Button on a remote
51 IRS info
53 Line of guards
55 Frenzied way to run
57 Group of pages that hasn't been updated
60 Festive fete
61 *The Lion in Winter* star
62 Neither companion
63 Jacuzzi effect
64 Without much strength
65 Hosp. fluid feeders

DOWN

1 Cry of despair
2 Football, informally
3 Putting on a pedestal
4 Elisabeth of *Leaving Las Vegas*
5 Track star Lewis
6 Comics bark
7 Slugging meas.
8 Informal chat
9 Therefore, to Descartes

10 Pvt.'s boss
11 Some inadmissible evidence
12 Fallen to pieces
13 Took home after taxes
18 Uncle of our country
22 Roof over a porch
25 Lion's locks
26 Not ___ long shot
28 Venetian blind strip
30 Motorless aircraft
31 Sum up
32 Black-ink item
36 Sneaky scheme
37 Ladd or Alda
38 Lost control
39 Completely unconscious
40 "Now playing ___ theater near you!"
41 Escape artist Harry
42 "Cocktail" namesake
43 Series starters
44 Disappointing desert "lake"
45 Deserving attention
49 Bride's new title
52 Garbage carrier
53 An amoeba has one
54 Follow the rules
56 Bandleader Kyser
58 Feathered stole
59 Stir-fry pan

138 POSTSEASON GAMES PEOPLE PLAY

ACROSS

1 Break in friendly relations
5 Splashy resort
8 English explorer Sebastian
13 Gardner of courtroom novels
14 Bert, to Ernie
15 Superior members
17 Postseason game for consommé lovers?
19 Noisy baby toy
20 Remove from office
21 "May ___ of service?"
23 Auctioneer's cry
24 Norman Bates' place
25 Z's, to Zorba the Greek
27 Farrow of *Rosemary's Baby*
28 Prior to, previously
29 The Beatles' "___ Fell"
31 Actress Liv
33 Period
35 Tavern
37 They exist
38 Postseason game for boxers?
41 Going wrong
44 Kareem, as a kid
45 Enumeration abbr.

48 Go in again
50 "Dutch" tree
52 Radio operator
54 Suitable
55 Satellite path
57 Hill of hearings
59 Daytime TV drama
61 Life sci.
62 Lacking a key, musically
63 Igloo inhabitant
65 Clean postseason game?
67 Show uncertainty
68 Pugilist Muhammad
69 Grease job
70 Wolf's warning
71 Fishing boat tool
72 *"L'___, c'est moi"*

DOWN

1 Applicant's offering
2 Raw steel
3 Disconcert
4 Native American abode
5 Lady Macbeth's problem
6 Feline foot, e.g.
7 Kate's sitcom companion
8 Postseason game for flakes?
9 It's north of Fla.
10 Tiny pieces
11 Footstool or Turk

12 Revelatory
16 Family cars
18 Indonesian island
22 Air conditioner meas.
25 Metal used in ointment
26 Great deal
30 Digital postseason game?
32 Four-minute run, perhaps
34 "... hear ___ drop"
36 New York Rangers' org.
39 Golden Rule preposition
40 Red vegetable
41 Removes chalk dust
42 Lies at rest
43 Captured again
46 Reduce in number
47 Grape used in winemaking
49 Stat for a slugger
51 Geometry or trig
53 Xylophone striker
56 Hawkeye
58 Commoner counterpart
60 Tilting tower town
62 ___ were
64 Put a scuff on
66 Schooner contents

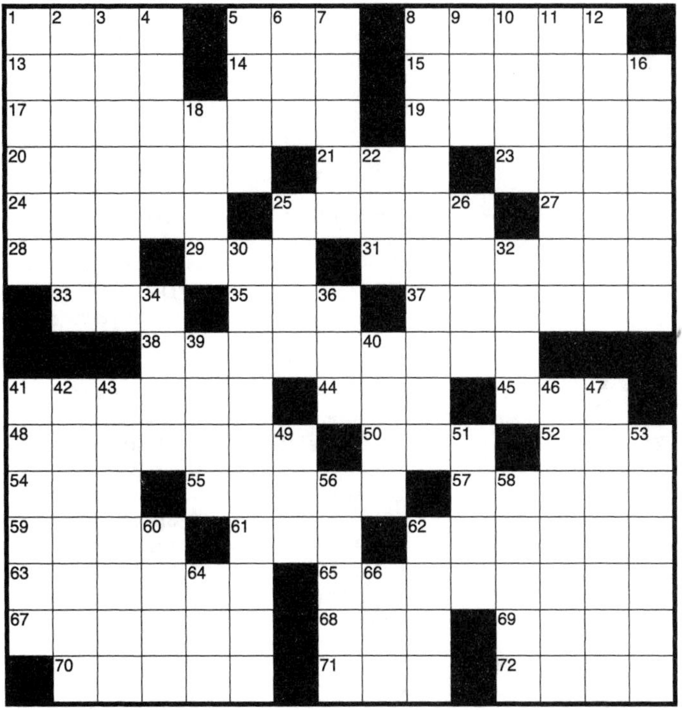

139 NOW PLAYING AT THE MEGAPLEX

ACROSS
1 Lite
6 1982 Jeff Bridges movie
10 Omar of *House*
14 Redden the face of
15 Home of Baylor University
16 Baseball Hall of Famer Speaker
17 1989 Spike Lee movie
20 Shepherd's locale
21 Character parts?
22 Rosie's fastener
23 Immigrant's subj.
24 Played the copycat
25 ___ Raton, Florida
26 Cannonballs and bullets
28 1997 Morgan Freeman movie
31 "The Divine Miss M"
33 Finishes third
35 Ambient musician Brian
36 Gets down
37 Avoids like the plague
38 "Yeah, sure"
39 Go awry
40 Try to avoid a tag
41 Lerner's partner in musicals

42 1986 Oliver Stone movie
44 City on the Rhine
45 Revolver brand
46 Like a church mouse
48 Bush or Stuart
51 Go one better than
53 Tied up
54 GI mail drop
55 1959 Bob Hope movie
58 Shoelace problem
59 Give relief to a thief
60 Harvard, Yale, etc.
61 Right in the head
62 1981 Warren Beatty movie
63 Smart set

DOWN
1 Big dipper
2 Double-reed instruments
3 1993 Glenn Close movie
4 Cigar residue
5 1997 Michael Douglas film
6 Strong string
7 Went ballistic
8 Phil of folk
9 Part of NIMBY
10 Wrong-and-right field

11 1980 Goldie Hawn movie
12 Needle dropper
13 NCO rank
18 Bank take-back
19 Un plus deux
25 Yuppie wheels
27 Everest and St. Helens
28 Top-drawer
29 De novo
30 Spoil, with "on"
31 Roadrunner sound
32 Scruggs of C&W
33 Place for a splint
34 1963 Paul Newman movie
37 Space on a schedule
38 It's tiny and attractive
40 Flies alone
41 1965 Peter O'Toole movie
43 As of now
44 Rover's reward
46 Put forward
47 Topples from power
49 Tools for duels
50 "Blame It on the ___ Nova"
51 Acorn producers
52 Wrist-elbow connector
53 Neuwirth of *Chicago*
56 Cookie holder
57 Hadrian's "Hail!"

140 GENDER-NEUTRAL POETS

ACROSS

1 Lanka lead-in
4 Financing abbr.
7 *Nova* network
10 Belle of the ball
13 Spy novelist John
15 Partner for high
17 At great length
18 More haughty
19 Gender-neutral poet?
21 Seam contents
22 Cockpit abbr.
23 Ice house: Var.
26 At least one
27 Tips, as a hat
32 Letter before sigma
33 Keep a leaky boat afloat
35 Prove successful
36 Gender-neutral poet?
39 One way to fall
40 Ring, as a bell
41 Great score
42 Ill-tempered
43 AC capacity measure
44 Cancún coin
45 Cry companion
46 "... and seven years ___"
48 Gender-neutral poet?
57 Doing very well

58 Pip's *Great Expectations* love
59 Not in custody
60 Information sources
61 Word in many commandments
62 *The Beggar's Opera* writer
63 Streaker of old
64 Morse bit

DOWN

1 Mess maker
2 Kevin's *Tin Cup* costar
3 Confident words
4 Intense devotion
5 Inclined
6 Gamblers' mecca
7 Easy out, often
8 Explode
9 Cease and desist
10 "___ ask for your opinion?"
11 Forbidden fruit garden
12 *Titanic* obstacle
14 Pear variety
16 California's Big ___
20 Star's mail
23 *Rich Man Poor Man* novelist Shaw

24 Accra's country
25 Lounges
26 Help out
27 Chocolate factory creator Roald
28 *Double Fantasy* artist
29 Strong point
30 Circuit protection
31 Kind of pad
33 Large group
34 "We ___ Family"
35 Homeboy
37 Wee one
38 Musical Reed
43 Tobacco type
44 Sponge features
45 Andrew Wyeth subject
46 Church nooks
47 Bother
48 Rivers of comedy
49 Not taken in by
50 "Hold it right there!"
51 FDR program
52 *Star Trek* assimilators
53 They have boughs for bows
54 Eskimo transport
55 It's a crock
56 Graham of rock

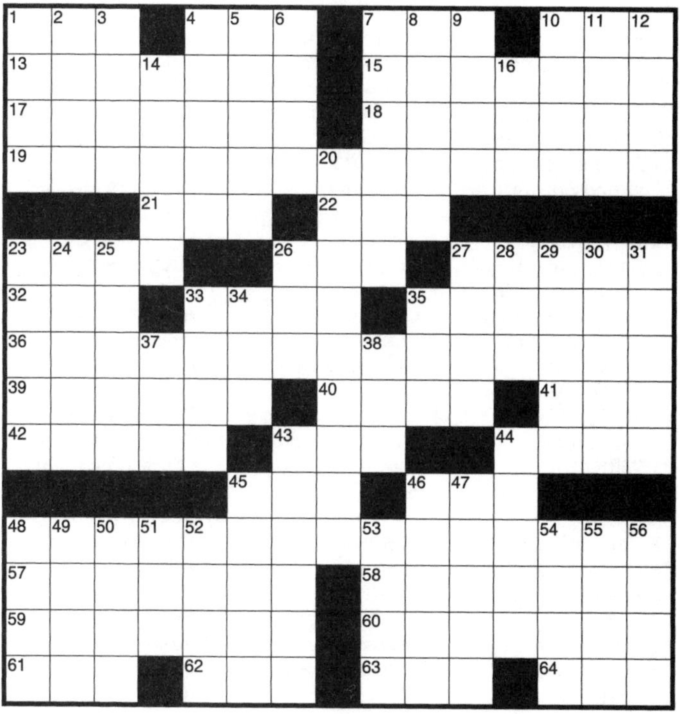

141 THEY DO AND I DO

ACROSS

1 Type of box or joint
5 Rice dish
10 Stock responses?
14 As one, at Orly
15 "Ready or not, here ___!"
16 Play opener
17 Boy Scouts do this
19 "I Love Rock 'n Roll" singer Joan
20 Cow owner of fiery lore
21 Dorm VIPs
23 My ___, Vietnam
24 Sacked out
25 With 48-Across, moviegoers do this
27 Thailand, once
28 *Chitty Chitty Bang Bang* screenwriter Roald
30 Tiny amounts
31 Blockhead
32 Erato or Urania
33 Paul Newman role in *Exodus*
34 Divers do this
39 Jimmy and Rosalynn's daughter
40 Castile neighbor
41 Blockhead
43 George Jetson's dog
46 XL, e.g.
47 Type of dancer in a discotheque
48 See 25-Across

50 Soup server
51 Superman's nemesis Luthor
52 McClanahan of *The Golden Girls*
53 Contract provision
55 Venus de Milo's lack
57 Horses do this
60 Some writers work on it
61 Benefit
62 Georgetown athlete
63 Ride-seeker's cry
64 Satisfy, as a debt
65 Neglected, as a debt

DOWN

1 Protrude
2 One who's for labor or against secession
3 Polish sausage
4 Regard
5 Yacht spot
6 Like a glue spill
7 First name in horror films
8 Ethically indifferent
9 Type of position
10 Houlihan's *M*A*S*H* rank
11 Leopardlike cat
12 Canadian capital
13 Demonstrations
18 Made a fool of
22 Slippery slope

24 Bible book before Jer.
25 Biker's hot-dog maneuver
26 Bump off
28 "When ___ whispers low 'Thou must' ...": Emerson
29 Fireplace remains
32 *A Million Little Pieces*, e.g.
33 Balm ingredient
35 Supergirl's Krypton name
36 Candy brand
37 "Nice going!" in Nottingham
38 Keen visual sense
42 One on the other side
43 After a long wait
44 Everest guide, often
45 Like some cuisine of the Southwest
46 Place to hide an ace
47 Pampas cowpoke
49 Beet or cane extract
50 Back muscle, briefly
53 Pet plant
54 Tomlin of *All of Me*
56 Bio. or chem.
58 Keg outlet
59 Paul Sorvino, to Mira

142 THE REEL THING

ACROSS

1 "You've Made ___ Very Happy"
5 Refrigerator gas
10 Performs
14 Declare openly
15 Get the idea
16 "Confound it!"
17 Reel people?
19 Hoopla
20 Govt. property overseer
21 "My stars!"
22 O'Donnell of *A League of Their Own*
23 Ticked off
25 The reel thing?
28 Fired up
29 "___ and away!"
30 Aviation hero
31 Eases off of, with "from"
33 With 35-Across, part of every protein
34 Little guy
35 See 33-Across
37 Unfashionable fellow
39 Cable channel
42 Like a lot
44 Small sample
48 Anger
49 "Fancy" singer McEntire
50 With very little fat
51 Reel property?

54 Home of the Hurricanes
55 Make corrections to
56 Go on an animal's back
58 Droop
59 Stale Italian bread?
60 It's reel nice?
63 One way to start
64 Nut for pies
65 Cartoon light-bulb indication
66 *Chicago* star Richard
67 Brundage of the Olympics
68 Untouchable Eliot

DOWN

1 O'Neal's *Love Story* costar
2 Slippery
3 Mogadishu's country
4 Have debts
5 Old Glory, for example
6 Summary
7 Vibrating membrane
8 Mined find
9 U-turn from SSE
10 For a special purpose
11 High-class glass

12 Pudding ingredient
13 Used a rudder
18 Dreaded ink color
22 School assignment
24 *Show Boat* author Ferber
26 Give your two cents' worth
27 Month of many marriages
32 Filled with fright
33 Sun-dried brick
36 Fateful day for Caesar
38 Painter Salvador
39 Period in between
40 Brine by-product
41 More harsh
43 Mad scramble
45 Coastal region
46 They're wrapped in corn husks
47 Riddles
52 Filled with wonder
53 Indian instrument
54 Type of school for doctors
57 Contradict
60 Phi Beta Kappa concern, for short
61 Gun
62 Aircraft stabilizer

143 **3 45s**

ACROSS

1 Crumple, with "up"
4 Shari, Jerry, or Gary
9 Touched down
13 Parched
15 Words of refusal
16 ___-tat
17 .45
20 One who serves a dictator?
21 A radius is part of it
22 Satisfied sighs
23 "Yuck!"
26 Where to see R.E.M.
27 Lend a hand to
29 Electrical unit
31 Goes down in defeat
33 Wood-dressing tool
34 "I was elsewhere" excuse
36 *Titanic* dangers
37 45
41 Wind direction finders
42 Instruct
43 Top 40 songs
44 "For sure!"
46 43,560 square feet
50 Cause of sick leave, perhaps
51 Vigoda of *Barney Miller*
52 Big name in bouquets

54 Denom.
55 Type of yeast
58 "Let ___ hang out"
60 '45
63 Bauxite and others
64 *Annie Get Your Gun* star Merman
65 It's sold in sticks
66 Singer Arnold
67 *La ___ Vita*
68 Concorde, for one

DOWN

1 Polish capital
2 Singer Franklin
3 Sell off
4 Ullmann of *Autumn Sonata*
5 Ma'am to a lamb
6 Klingon on the *Enterprise*
7 What one makes
8 Fits companion
9 Diva's piece
10 Type of retriever
11 Used Schedule A
12 "Glue" for feathers
14 Yankee first baseman Mattingly
18 Yankee first baseman Gehrig
19 Bible book after Ex.
24 Smooth-talking
25 Freddie the Freeloader, e.g.

28 ___ Moines, Iowa
30 Resembles, with "after"
32 Mile-a-minute speed
33 Word of welcome
35 Article from Arles
36 Broadcast-regulating org.
37 Cooler resident
38 "Leave no stone ___"
39 Underwater hazard
40 Dawn direction
41 From 30 to 300 MHz
44 Complied with commands
45 *From ___ Eternity*
47 Moves on hands and knees
48 Depends
49 Cass of the Mamas & the Papas
51 Hole maker
53 "What's the ___?"
56 How some take it
57 Canadian comedian Mort
59 Tango number
60 Military enemy
61 Fun and games, for short
62 Bullring bellow

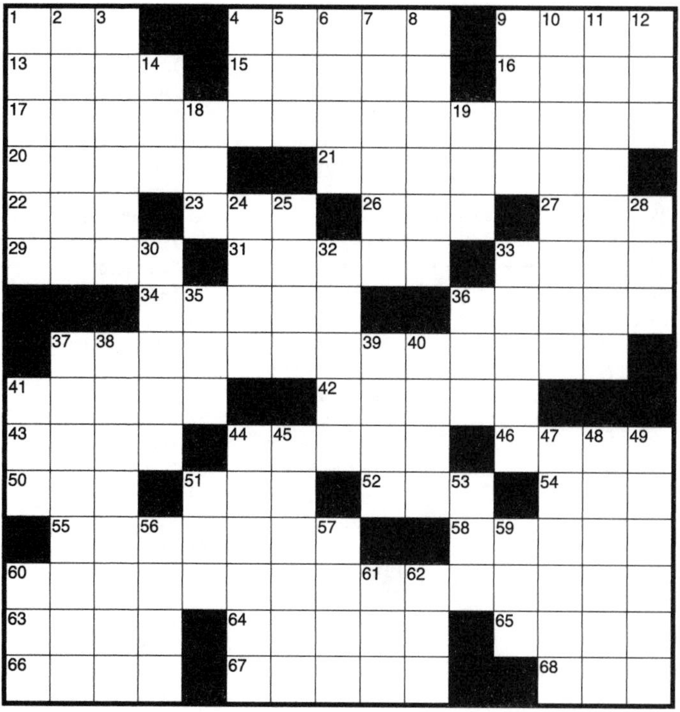

144 ONLINE CONNECTIONS

ACROSS
1 Fruit drink ending
4 Suds seller
9 Sumter and Knox
14 Tattoo word, perhaps
15 Put on cloud nine
16 Go gaga over
17 "What ___, chopped liver?"
18 Levy on fuel
20 Mag for enthusiasts
22 "___ you loud and clear!"
23 Flirt with persistently, with "on"
24 Kind of mind
27 Pat of *The Karate Kid*
29 Sergeant, for example
30 *Titanic* director James
31 Retired flier
32 Leg bone
35 Blowgun ammo
36 All tuckered out
39 Bee flat?
42 Vocalist Tucker
43 Flower shop letters
46 Like Miss Congeniality
49 Shoot for, with "to"
51 Bullock of *Miss Congeniality*
52 Pitch source
54 FBI employee

55 Detective Pinkerton
57 Hop, skip, or jump
58 Type of comb for going over things
62 OR workers
63 Like krypton
64 Mink wrap
65 Malt drink
66 Sportscaster Bradshaw
67 Protest that no one would stand for?
68 It connects the words of five answers in this puzzle

DOWN
1 Women warriors
2 Pizza chain
3 Distinguished
4 Hard throw, in baseball
5 The Crimson Tide's st.
6 Computer language
7 Baby bird?
8 Prefix with prompter
9 Enthusiasts collectively
10 Verse on a vase
11 Tax-sheltered nest egg
12 Benedict Arnold, for one
13 Navigating instrument

19 Paul Simon's "___ Rock"
21 And so on, for short
25 Rooter preceder
26 Infamous Ugandan
28 Comedian Foxx
30 Genesis perpetrator
33 ___ noire
34 Give ___ go
36 Rosary component
37 Tatum's dad
38 Facility
39 Loses it
40 John Lennon song
41 Wine seller
43 Hook and ladder rider
44 It requires footwork
45 Placed far in
47 Like Dennis the Menace
48 *Mission: Impossible* theme composer Schifrin
50 Jim and Tammy's old org.
52 Page of music?
53 ___ water (imperiled)
56 Quarterback sack result
59 Drop the ball
60 Gin maker Whitney
61 Cub scout unit

254

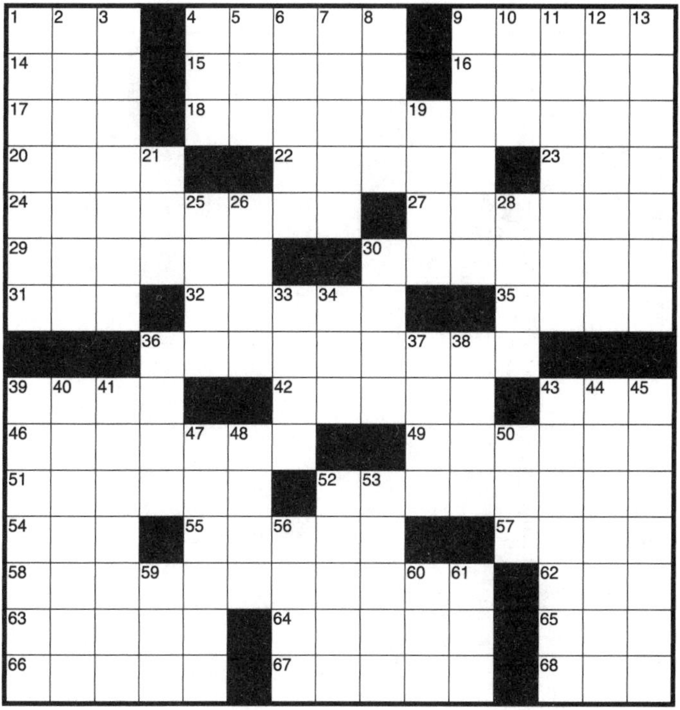

1

O	B	E	S	E	■	A	R	A	B
R	A	R	I	N	G	T	O	G	O
T	R	I	N	I	L	O	P	E	Z
O	R	C	■	D	I	N	E	R	O
N	I	C	E	■	B	A	L	E	■
■	C	A	L	L	■	L	A	L	O
C	A	R	V	E	S	■	D	A	D
A	D	M	I	T	T	E	D	T	O
P	E	E	R	T	O	P	E	E	R
E	D	N	A	■	W	A	R	D	S

2

S	O	L	I	D	■	A	L	E	E
E	R	I	C	A	■	N	U	L	L
R	A	Z	E	R	■	N	I	L	E
B	L	A	C	K	M	A	G	I	C
■	■	A	R	A	B	I	S	T	■
E	R	A	S	U	R	E	■	■	■
J	U	S	T	M	Y	L	U	C	K
E	M	I	L	■	A	L	C	O	A
C	O	D	E	■	N	E	L	L	Y
T	R	E	S	■	N	E	A	T	O

3

P	A	L	L	B	E	A	R	E	R
A	R	M	O	R	P	L	A	T	E
M	E	N	U	O	P	T	I	O	N
■	■	■	I	T	S	A	S	I	N
S	M	A	S	H	■	■	I	L	E
C	O	T	■	■	T	U	N	E	S
A	R	A	B	I	A	N	■	■	■
R	A	R	E	S	T	A	M	P	S
F	L	A	T	T	E	R	I	E	S
S	E	X	H	O	R	M	O	N	E

4

S	T	O	O	G	E	■	E	S	S
S	A	N	D	R	A	■	N	I	T
E	R	O	D	E	S	■	B	R	R
■	■	N	E	T	W	A	R	E	■
S	E	V	E	N	P	I	N	E	S
E	X	I	S	T	E	N	C	E	S
M	U	G	S	H	O	T	■	■	■
I	D	I	■	U	R	E	S	T	I
T	E	L	■	M	I	R	R	O	R
E	D	S	■	B	A	S	I	N	S

5

C	R	O	W	E	■	O	D	A	Y
O	A	T	E	N	■	P	I	L	E
A	G	I	N	G	■	E	G	O	S
X	A	C	T	O	K	N	I	F	E
■	■	O	R	I	E	N	T	S	■
C	L	A	N	G	E	D	■	■	■
F	U	L	L	E	F	F	E	C	T
L	I	L	I	■	F	I	B	E	R
A	G	I	N	■	E	R	O	D	E
T	I	N	E	■	R	E	N	E	E

6

A	M	O	S	■	K	A	R	E	L
B	I	G	W	I	N	N	E	R	S
U	N	L	I	C	E	N	S	E	D
S	T	A	S	H	E	S	■	■	■
E	E	L	S	■	D	O	R	K	S
D	R	A	F	T	■	T	H	E	N
■	■	■	R	A	T	H	O	L	E
M	O	R	A	L	S	E	N	S	E
D	R	I	N	K	O	R	D	E	R
S	Y	N	C	S	■	N	A	Y	S

7

```
Z Z T O P ■ S A P S
H E A V Y ■ E M I T
O U T E R S P A C E
U S E R A C T I O N
■ ■ ■ M E A N T O
F I T S I N ■ ■ ■
R O U N D T A B L E
I N P O S I T I O N
L I A R ■ N I K O N
L A C E ■ G E E N A
```

8

```
P A S S ■ C O O E R
O T T O ■ H I T M E
T H I N K A L O U D
P E N N E R ■ ■ ■
I N T E R C R O S S
E A S T P O I N T E
■ ■ ■ L A T E E N
U S E F U L T I P S
K E Y I N ■ E D I E
E W E E K ■ R A N D
```

9

```
E Q U A L ■ A L A S
A U N T I E M A M E
T O R O N T O S U N
■ O P E N N E S S
U L M ■ ■ A G R E E
N A A C P ■ T D S
I N N U E N D O ■ ■
T I T O P U E N T E
A N I M A L F E E D
S A C O ■ L Y R E S
```

10

```
B O B B Y D A R I N
I B E L I E V E S O
N O T U P T O P A R
D E A R ■ A T E I N
■ ■ ■ Y I E L D S
T A S S E L ■ ■ ■
E L E N A ■ L I A R
R O G E R W I L C O
S H E L L A C K E D
E A R L Y Y E A R S
```

11

```
R U M O R ■ J I B E
A T O N E ■ E T A S
P A R E D ■ W A L T
S H A F T ■ E L S E
■ ■ L I A R L I A R
S W I N G E R A ■
H A Z E ■ L Y N D A
A V I D ■ A B I E S
L E N A ■ C O C A S
E D G Y ■ E X E R T
```

12

```
S C R A T C H P A D
T R A D E R O U T E
J A Z Z S I N G E R
U N I ■ T S K ■ ■
D E N S ■ P A S S E
E D G E S ■ T E E M
■ ■ W A R ■ D A B
B A N A N A R A M A
I M A G E M A K E R
T I G E R S H A R K
```

257

13

```
P A R K A   C L E F
S T A I N   H A Z E
A W I N G   O K R A
L A N G E   R E A R
M R S C L A U S
    T O O L S H E D
S L O B   I L O V E
P U R R   S I R E E
A L M A   O N E N D
M U S S   N E S T S
```

14

```
A V O W E D   M G M
L I G H T O P E R A
S O L O C A R E E R
O L E S   B A S E L
    H A L T E R S
B A R O N E T
A B E T S   L U I S
S A N J A C I N T O
A B E R R A N T L Y
L A W   A N G O L A
```

15

```
G A L E   S H A K O
I D O L   T A P O N
J A N E P O W E L L
O P E N I N G D A Y
E T R A D E
    D H A R M A
P A G E L A Y O U T
O N E T I M E U S E
P E R O N   A S K S
E W I N G   R E S T
```

16

```
H O O C H   F O I E
A S S E E N O N T V
I S L E R O Y A L E
R I O S   F E L L S
Y E N   H U R L
    O R A N   S G T
A P R I L   H I R E
D O W N L O A D E D
E R A S E R H E A D
S K Y E   T A S T Y
```

17

```
T U B A   A S S A Y
I L L B E T H E R E
S M I L E S U P O N
    T A L E   T U T
B U Z Z   A R E N A
A S K E D   E N D S
F E R   O F A N
F R I E N D L I E R
L I E D O R M A N T
E D G A R   S L O E
```

18

```
O F A L L K I N D S
N O M E A N F E A T
O P E N S E S A M E
    N O T E   T A W
C H A R S   S A G E
R U B E   P O S E D
U R L   G A M A
C R E P E P A P E R
E A T E N A L I V E
S H O R E L I N E S
```

19

```
L O T T A   B A J A
A R Y A N   I G O R
M E R C I   G A L L
B O O K M O B I L E
      H A V A N A S
I D E A T E D
S U M M E R W I N D
A T O M   L O V E R
A C T E   I L O N A
C H E R   E F R E M
```

20

```
A R B O R V I T A E
C U R T A I N R O D
M E A T E A T E R S
E S T     C O N T E
      F R O N T A L
S P A R E M E
F R E E D     C W T
B O I S E I D A H O
A V O C A D O D I P
Y O U A R E H E R E
```

21

```
C H I P   P O L K A
R E D H E R R I N G
A L L O W E D F O R
I L E N E     T W A
G O R I L L A
      C L A V E L L
A L I   V E N U E
J U D D H I R S C H
A C E V E N T U R A
R E A D Y   S E E R
```

22

```
G A E L   P O I S E
E L S E   A C R E S
R E C A P T U R E S
I C A N R E L A T E
    P E E   A T O N
A G E D   S R I
M E M O R Y L O S S
I N E V I D E N C E
G E N E T   N A S A
A S T R A   S L I M
```

23

```
C A M P   A R C E D
U R G E   M O L A R
R I M S   E M O R Y
L A S T   L A S
U N T I D I N E S S
P A U L A A B D U L
    D E N   A B B E
P A I N S   T O T E
A M O C O   H O L T
R I S E N   S K Y S
```

24

```
T V V C R   S C A D
R A I M I   H A L O
E L D O C T O R O W
E V E N H A N D E D
D E O   A M E S
    G A R P   H E S
S T A N D A P A R T
T O M O S B O R N E
A G E D   A R K I N
N O S E   Y E S E S
```

25

```
L B J F R E E W A Y
I R E L A N D E R S
M U T A N T G E N E
E S T   C H A S E R
S H Y   H U R
      U S S   L A B
A V A N T I   O V A
B E L L Y A C H E S
A N G E L S H A R K
S T A T E M E N T S
```

26

```
B I G M A C   S T S
E N R I C H   P O P
T R A N C E   I M A
S E T T O   O R C S
  G U E S T R O O M
F A I R T R I A L
O R T S   A N G L E
I D O   A D O N I S
S T U   R E C E N T
T O S   B R O W S E
```

27

```
T R A   A L I B I S
I I M A G I N E S O
O P E N L E T T E R
G O N N A   R H E E
A N D O R R A
      T E E N A G E
E T T A   E S T A S
F O R T I F I E R S
G R O O V E T U B E
H A T R E D   P O X
```

28

```
M A R E   W A H O O
I B E X   A T O L L
C O A X   B A L E D
A R L O   B L E S S
S T E N C I L S
    S M U T T I E R
A C T O R   I N R E
S L A B S   M O N A
O U T I E   E N I D
F E E L S   S E E S
```

29

```
S A P S   S T O A T
H U L A   W A U G H
O R A L   A R T I E
D A Y S C H O O L S
    S A R I   N E E
A L A   A L F A
G O L D F I E L D S
A B O U T   D I E T
P E N N E   E M M Y
E D G E D   X B O X
```

30

```
I M A C   A T B A T
N A T I O N A L L Y
K N O C K K N O C K
S A M A R A   W O E
    I D A   B I A S
C O C A   B A N
A R M   B O L G E R
L E A V E A L O N E
L O S E G R O U N D
A S S E S   U T E S
```

31

I	N	N	E	R		S	A	G	A
C	O	O	L	E		Q	U	I	D
A	D	L	I	B		U	E	L	E
M	A	T	Z	O	B	A	L	L	S
E	L	E	A	Z	A	R			
			B	O	Z	E	M	A	N
M	A	K	E	S	A	F	A	C	E
E	M	I	T		A	O	R	T	A
S	E	T	H		R	O	T	O	R
A	N	T	I		S	T	A	R	S

32

F	A	I	R		C	H	E	E	K
A	R	C	H		Y	O	G	I	C
C	I	A	O		B	W	A	N	A
T	E	R	N		I	D	L	E	R
S	L	E	E	K	L	Y			
			W	I	L	D	E	S	T
R	A	D	I	O		O	N	T	O
E	V	A	N	S		O	N	O	R
D	E	R	E	K		D	I	G	S
D	R	E	S	S		Y	O	Y	O

33

J	U	A	R	E	Z		F	A	Q
A	D	H	E	R	E		A	B	U
M	E	A	S	U	R	A	B	L	E
			E	P	O	X	I	E	S
B	R	A	N	T		L	A	S	T
R	E	S	T		G	E	N	T	S
A	T	H	E	A	R	T			
C	O	L	D	W	A	R	E	R	A
T	O	E		E	V	E	L	Y	N
S	K	Y		D	E	E	M	E	D

34

E	D	G	E		R	A	C	K	S
L	A	R	A		E	N	O	L	A
S	M	A	R	T	M	O	N	E	Y
I	O	N		R	A	I	S	E	S
E	N	D	P	O	I	N	T		
		J	A	U	N	T	I	E	R
L	O	U	I	S	E		T	R	E
E	A	R	N	E	D	R	U	N	S
S	H	O	E	R		A	T	I	T
S	U	R	D	S		T	E	E	S

35

C	O	N	C	U	R		B	A	N
I	D	E	A	T	E		A	V	A
T	E	X	M	E	X		S	I	B
E	S	T	E	R		S	I	L	O
		T	R	U	C	K	C	A	B
S	W	O	O	S	H	E	D		
K	I	L	N		E	E	R	I	E
I	D	A		A	R	T	E	S	T
R	E	S		L	I	E	S	T	O
T	N	T		P	E	R	S	O	N

36

R	O	S	E	Q	U	A	R	T	Z
O	U	T	N	U	M	B	E	R	S
T	R	A	D	E	M	E	D	I	A
		L	O	B		D	I	T	Z
S	T	E	R	E	S		R	E	S
H	A	M		C	A	M	E	R	A
E	T	A	S		V	A	C		
R	A	T	A	T	A	T	T	A	T
P	R	E	V	E	N	T	E	R	S
A	S	S	E	N	T	E	D	T	O

37

N	A	G	S	■	M	I	X	U	P
E	L	I	A	■	I	N	A	N	E
O	F	F	B	A	L	A	N	C	E
N	A	T	U	R	E	W	A	L	K
■	■	■	■	A	P	E	X	E	S
A	K	I	M	B	O	■	■	■	■
L	E	D	D	I	S	P	L	A	Y
C	A	L	L	A	T	R	U	C	E
O	N	E	I	N	■	O	K	R	A
A	U	D	I	S	■	P	E	E	R

38

S	K	A	T	■	H	I	L	D	A
P	O	L	I	C	E	R	A	I	D
E	C	O	N	O	L	O	D	G	E
C	H	E	E	R	I	N	E	S	S
K	I	S	S	U	P	■	■	■	■
■	■	■	S	O	M	A	L	I	■
B	A	S	I	C	R	A	T	E	S
A	L	L	N	A	T	U	R	A	L
S	P	O	R	T	S	L	I	N	E
T	E	P	E	E	■	S	A	S	S

39

M	A	D	T	V	■	A	D	I	M
I	D	A	H	O	■	N	O	R	A
N	O	V	E	L	I	D	E	A	S
E	R	E	C	T	O	R	S	E	T
O	N	T	O	■	N	O	B	■	■
■	■	H	M	M	■	M	E	G	A
A	B	O	M	I	N	A	T	O	R
C	O	M	I	C	A	C	T	O	R
E	V	A	S	■	S	H	E	S	A
D	A	S	H	■	H	E	R	E	S

40

E	D	E	R	■	O	L	D	E	R
L	A	M	A	■	D	U	E	T	O
I	N	A	B	E	Y	A	N	C	E
J	U	J	I	T	S	U	■	■	■
A	B	O	D	E	S	■	M	E	R
H	E	R	■	R	E	N	A	M	E
■	■	■	U	N	Y	O	K	E	D
S	O	B	S	I	S	T	E	R	S
I	N	L	E	T	■	E	D	I	E
R	E	T	R	Y	■	S	O	L	A

41

T	I	D	E	■	D	A	R	T	H
O	N	O	R	B	E	F	O	R	E
G	A	N	G	O	F	F	O	U	R
A	N	T	■	B	E	A	T	E	R
S	E	G	A	■	R	I	C	■	■
■	■	O	R	D	■	R	A	G	S
S	C	A	L	I	A	■	U	R	I
L	O	W	E	R	C	A	S	E	D
O	R	A	N	G	E	P	E	E	L
P	A	Y	E	E	■	E	S	T	E

42

S	P	A	C	E	A	L	I	E	N
P	E	C	C	A	D	I	L	L	O
A	N	T	I	S	O	V	I	E	T
■	N	A	V	Y	B	E	A	N	S
■	■	■	T	O	S	C	A	■	■
■	P	A	P	A	S	■	■	■	■
C	A	M	E	R	A	B	A	G	■
U	N	A	R	G	U	A	B	L	E
L	E	P	R	E	C	H	A	U	N
P	L	A	Y	T	E	S	T	E	D

43

```
O L D A S M E T H U S E L A H
H E I R T O T H E T H R O N E
M O D E R A T E D R I N K E R
S N O . I N E . Y E N . I T S
. . . U P I . . . C E O . . .
D A M P E N S . S H R I V E L
E W E S . G O T A T . L I R A
G I L T . L A Y . S C A T
A S E A . S O U S A . E A S E
S H E R P A S . O R D E R E R
. . . T A M . . . C I D . . .
C E E . G O P . G A S . S H A
U N L E A V E N E D B R E A D
E T E R N A L T R I A N G L E
D R E S S R E H E A R S A L S
```

44

```
L A B E L S . A S S O O N A S
A M U L E T . R A I N I E S T
U P R O A R . A N T E L O P E
R E L I N E . I S A . N I N
E R A S E S . O T B . N A R C
L E P E R S . P A Y . U T A H
. . . S E D E R . . M A N E
M O C K . S O N I C . B L T S
A B O O . N O A H S . . .
R E N O . B T U . A P P A L L
T I C K . I T T . S A L V I A
I S L . G L O . T W A I N S
N A U T I L U S . I N N A T E
I N D I R E C T . S E T T E R
S T E A L T H Y . E D S E L S
```

45

```
S E A F A R I N G . P O L L S
A L L I G A T O R . U R I A H
T E T E A T E T E . T R A C E
E C O L I . M E G . T I R E D
. . . D N A . . . V I N . . .
S O P . S T S . F E N . I V E
T R A C T I O N E N G I N E S
A I R C O N D I T I O N E R S
L O S I N G O N E S N E R V E
E N E . E L M . S O T . T E X
. . . S S E . . . N H L . . .
I K N O W . L O A . E L O P E
D H A B I . A L M A M A T E R
E A S E L . D E M E A N I N G
S N A R L . D O O R P O S T S
```

46

```
A C H E D . C A C T I . P A P
B R I N E . O L E A N . R N A
A O R T A . P O L K A D O T S
S N E R D . Y U L E T I D E S
H E R A L D . D O N . S I R E
. . . P Y R E . . O H G O D
T V S . S A D I R O N . I O O
O O H . I M I T A T E . E M U
O L A . N A T A S H A . S S T
L U R E S . . P E T S . . .
I M E T . P T S . R A T T A N
N E C T A R I N E . T O R S O
G O R E V I D A L . I N A W E
U N O . O Z A R K . M E D A L
P E P . W E L L S . E D E N S
```

47

```
A L A   E M O T I V E   M A J
N I L   S O L I D E R   E V A
I N A P P L E P I E O R D E R
M E M E N T O   E R O D I N G
A M E N           S A G O
L A D   R A M   O H S   T E N
S N A P O N E S F I N G E R S
      O P E R E T T A S
T A N G E R I N E O R A N G E
H E E   S A T   N N E   I A N
E R O S           A T R A
B A N A N A S   E P I G R A M
A T A D I S A D V A N T A G E
R O T   C O N C E R N   T E L
D R E   E N G I N E S   E S S
```

48

```
M A S T   A R M S D E A L E R
E T T E   R E A L E S T A T E
S T E T   P A R I S T E X A S
M I R E     S C I   M E T E
E T N A   S P H E R E   R S T
R U N T   T I A   E E N
I D E E   A L L S   G U L P S
Z E S T   Y E L P S   R E E K
E S S E N   S I R E   S A R I
      S O S   N E E   E D I T
T S E   M E R G E R   M I S T
H E L M   N A Y       A N C E
R E G I S T R A R S   I G O R
U N I L A T E R A L   D U P E
M O N E Y O R D E R   S P E D
```

49

```
A R M O R E D C A R   I S I S
Q U A R A N T I N E   A H M E
U N D I G E S T E D   N E H I
A L O E S     W A R   B O Z
T E N N   A L S   S E S A M E
I S N T   T E A M   M A N E
C S A   C O N N O T I N G
      L O N G J O H N S
    F I N E T U N E D   P E P
  B E E F   H A I R   A R N O
F E N N E L   N E E   R O T S
A R C   R E C     S A V E S
T A I L   D R Y A S A B O N E
A T N O   G U I T A R I S T S
L E G O   E X P A T I A T E S
```

50

```
T E R M E D   G A D   D O T H
E X H A L E   I F I   E P E E
A C I D I C   G I V E S E A R
S E N A T E   I C E R I N K S
E L E M E N T   I S A   H E H
      T A R O T   N O T I
A S T A B   K E N   R O U T S
P O R N O   E T A   A I S L E
A C I N G   T A D   G R E E R
R I P E   O H G O D
T A T   R U E   S A D D E N S
F L Y I N G B Y   N O R M A L
R I C K S H A W   G R O O V E
O T H E   T I C   L I S T E D
M E S S   A T A   E A S E L S
```

51

Q	U	A	Y		N	O	I	S	E	M	A	K	E	R
U	T	N	E		I	N	F	I	N	I	T	I	V	E
I	A	N	S		N	E	A	P	O	L	I	T	A	N
T	H	O	N	G		S	T	S		E	M	E	N	D
		O	R	E			E	S	E					
S	D	S		A	N	T		S	T	P		I	C	I
P	R	E	S	I	D	E	N	T	R	E	A	G	A	N
E	A	T	O	N	E	S	H	E	A	R	T	O	U	T
A	M	A	N	C	A	L	L	E	D	H	O	R	S	E
R	A	E		A	R	A		L	E	O		S	E	L
			M	R	S				S	U	M			
A	B	E	A	R		J	A	M		R	A	Z	E	S
R	E	A	N	I	M	A	T	O	R		G	O	A	T
T	A	R	G	E	T	D	A	T	E		N	O	S	Y
S	U	P	E	R	V	E	N	E	D		A	M	E	X

52

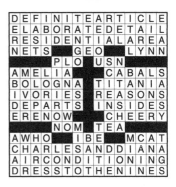

D	I	S	B	A	R			O	J	I	B	W	A
E	N	T	R	I	E	S		S	A	R	A	H	S
S	T	R	O	L	L	E	R		E	L	A	T	E	S
O	R	E	O	S		A	E	S		O	S	H	E	A
L	I	E	D		M	A	D	C	A	P		E	L	Y
A	C	T	I		U	N	H	O	L	Y				
T	A	M	E		G	E	E	U	P		S	A	S	S
E	T	A	S		M	R	T			A	L	O	U
D	E	P	T		N	O	R	M	S		S	P	U	N
			M	E	N	I	A	L		K	E	R	N
J	U	T		T	E	E	N	S	Y		A	N	T	I
A	T	A	L	E		S	G	T		E	T	H	A	N
P	I	R	A	T	E		S	E	T	L	O	O	S	E
A	C	O	R	N	S			R	E	S	O	R	T	S
N	A	S	D	A	Q			C	A	N	N	E	S

53

F	O	R	D	L	T	D		R	A	V	A	G	E	S
O	P	E	N	A	I	R		A	L	I	M	O	N	Y
R	E	M	A	R	R	Y		D	O	G	S	T	A	R
E	R	A		V	E	R	T	I	G	O		I	C	I
P	A	R	K	A		O	O	O		R	E	N	T	A
A	T	K	A		H	A	R	T	S		S	T	E	N
W	E	S	T		A	S	N	E	W		S	O	D	S
			S	T	A	L	E							
B	E	L	T		U	P	P	E	D		A	D	I	M
E	R	O	O		P	E	A	S	E		N	E	M	O
L	A	R	G	E		A	R	C		A	G	A	I	N
L	S	D		S	E	N	T	O	F	F		D	T	S
J	U	J	I	T	S	U		P	I	T	A	P	A	T
A	R	I	D	E	S	T		E	L	E	V	A	T	E
R	E	M	O	R	A	S		S	E	R	E	N	E	R

54

D	E	F	I	N	I	T	E	A	R	T	I	C	L	E
E	L	A	B	O	R	A	T	E	D	E	T	A	I	L
R	E	S	I	D	E	N	T	I	A	L	A	R	E	A
N	E	T	S		G	E	O		L	Y	N	N
			P	L	O		U	S	N					
A	M	E	L	I	A			C	A	B	A	L	S
B	O	L	O	G	N	A		T	I	T	A	N	I	A
I	V	O	R	I	E	S		R	E	A	S	O	N	S
D	E	P	A	R	T	S		I	N	S	I	D	E	S
E	R	E	N	O	W			C	H	E	E	R	Y
			N	O	M		T	E	A					
A	W	H	O		I	B	E		M	C	A	T
C	H	A	R	L	E	S	A	N	D	D	I	A	N	A
A	I	R	C	O	N	D	I	T	I	O	N	I	N	G
D	R	E	S	S	T	O	T	H	E	N	I	N	E	S

55

```
Z S A Z S A   C A U S E W A Y
E N T A I L   A L C A P O N E
B E T I D E   B U L G A R I A
R E A R E R S   M A E   K M S
A R R E S T E E       A B E T
          E X A M I N E
S T E E L E   P R E V E N T S
K I N D E R G A R T E N C O P
I N D I A N A N   A S T H M A
    A F F O R D S
Z A N Y       S I L E N C E R
E N G   B R A   R A V I O L I
L E E R I E S T   T E E M E D
I R R I T A T E   I N L I N E
G A S P E D A L   N A S C A R
```

56

```
S T A R B U C K S   S A C H S
H O N O R R O L L   A B H O R
I N I T I A L E R   M E O W S
N O M   E L E E   S P E C
  P A I R       A N A T O M Y
M U T T   B A R R E N   L I I
O R E S   A C U T E   W A S P
U P D O   L O P E Z   A T I P
R O C K   F R E R E   G E N E
N S A   H O N E Y S   E S S E
S E R I O U S     B R U T
    T S A R   N A P E   N R A
C H O I R   S O B E R E D U P
B O O N S   O V E R R E A C T
S I N G E   C A S T A N E T S
```

57

```
M A T A   S O B S   J O C K S
S T I C K E M U P   A P R O N
D A L A I L A M A   N E A T O
O L D S T E R   R A I N B O W
S L E E T S   B E S S
          C O A T   M I T T
A M E R I C A N D R E A M E R
C A L I F O R N I A S U I T E
C R O S S E N E M Y L I N E S
T E N K   R A T E
      A C T S   M O R O N S
G A L I L E I   P I L E S U P
E X I S T   O R A N G E A D E
R I F L E   N O S T A L G I C
E S T E R   S E T S   S E E S
```

58

```
E R S T   A W A S H   G T O S
S E E R   E R N I E   A R U N
P E R E   S I N E W   R O N A
O L G A   T I N   D U C K
S E E D   G E E N A   E P E E
I D A S   S U G A R I N E S S
T I N T   A P E   I N F
O N T H E   S T L   C U B I T
    E G G   Y I N   R E M O
C A R B O N C O P Y   N A P E
O R E O   P A U S E   I C E T
A L G A   M R T   T O D O
T E A R   A E G I S   U N I T
E N I D   T R U C E   R E N O
D E N S   L A N K A   E D G E
```

266

59

```
A T T A C H E C A S E ■ E M U
C O O R D I N A T E D ■ N A N
T Y P E S E T T E R S ■ D U B
R O M A ■ ■ ■ ■ E E Y O R E
E T A ■ S P E E D ■ L O R E N
S A S ■ A I S L E ■ U S E D
S S T ■ L A T E N ■ W R E N S
■ ■ S T F R A N C I S ■ ■ ■
A B E T S ■ A N I O N ■ C B S
L A N E ■ D O N H O ■ A R A
A L T E R ■ A R G O S ■ R O D
B O W L E G ■ ■ ■ ■ M O W N
A N I ■ M I N N I E M O U S E
M E N ■ A L B A T R O S S E S
A Y E ■ P A C E S E T T E R S
```

60

```
■ P R E F A B ■ J A C K I E
C R A Y O L A ■ A D R E N A L
L E V E R E D ■ R E U N I T E
I B I S E S ■ ■ E X O T I C
C O O ■ ■ P O T ■ ■ I N T
H I L O ■ T R U S S ■ C A T O
E L I Z A B E T H T A Y L O R
■ ■ O M I S S I O N S ■ ■
A S A N A L T E R N A T I V E
S A N E ■ L O T T E ■ S T E M
P I G ■ ■ S S S ■ ■ E N O
E L O P E D ■ ■ E S P R I T
C O L L I E R ■ A P P E A S E
T R A I N E E ■ L E A N T O S
■ S N E E R S ■ L E S S E N
```

61

```
P A S T O R A L A D D R E S S
A P A S S A G E T O I N D I A
R E P E A T E D O N E S E L F
E D S ■ G O D ■ P U T ■ R O E
■ ■ ■ M E N ■ ■ ■ T R E ■
A B B A S ■ T E A ■ I N D U E
L O O N ■ C O N N E C T O R S
G O O D F O R N O T H I N G S
A S T R O N A U T S ■ T H E E
E T H E R ■ H I E ■ F L O S S
■ ■ ■ L E G I ■ ■ D R E ■
S A M ■ W E B ■ E W E ■ T I P
A N I M A T E D G E S T U R E
A T T O R N E Y G E N E R A L
B E E I N O N E S B O N N E T
```

62

```
■ D E B A S E ■ H E A T H S
■ R E L E N T S ■ Y A R R O W
D O G M A T I C ■ P S E U D O
A B E T T E R ■ T N T ■ E G O
G E N R E S ■ O H O ■ E D E N
G R E E N ■ D I E T E D ■ ■
E T R E ■ M I L K I E S T ■
R O E ■ D E S P I S E ■ O U R
■ S I T A R I S T ■ N Y S E
■ F S T O P S ■ C O M E S ■
J U G S ■ I B E ■ S O M A L I
A T E ■ A N E ■ S T R I K E S
F U T I L E ■ P L A I N E S T
F R A C A S ■ J O I N E R S
E N T E R S ■ S E R G E S ■
```

63

C	Z	A	R	S		S	I	D	E	S	W	I	P	E
L	A	B	E	L		I	N	A	C	O	R	N	E	R
E	D	I	F	Y		T	O	R	T	O	I	S	E	S
R	O	D	I	N		U	N	T	O		T	O	R	E
I	R	E	N	E		P	E	S		D	E	M		
C	A	R	E	S	S				P	R	O	N	T	O
			S	T	E	L	M	O	S	F	I	R	E	
S	A	A	B		A	L	E	A	K		F	A	I	R
U	L	T	R	A	V	I	O	L	E	T				
E	S	T	A	T	E				R	E	G	A	R	D
		A	K	A		C	A	B		A	R	D	O	R
P	A	G	E		M	I	L	E		R	E	V	U	E
S	L	I	P	C	O	V	E	R		G	A	I	T	S
S	T	R	A	I	N	I	N	G		A	S	S	E	S
T	O	L	D	T	A	L	E	S		S	E	E	D	Y

64

	C	A	S	H	E	S		G	R	A	C	E	S	
D	O	N	K	E	Y	S		M	I	M	O	S	A	S
I	N	T	E	A	R	S		S	T	I	R	S	U	P
S	V	E	L	T	E				E	S	S	E	N	E
C	E	N	T	S		D	A	D		S	A	N	T	A
O	R	N	O		C	A	D	E	T		I	C	E	R
S	T	A	N	D	A	R	D	B	E	A	R	E	R	S
			O	R	L	E	A	N	S					
A	N	I	M	A	L	I	N	S	T	I	N	C	T	S
M	E	N	E		A	N	D	E	S		O	R	A	N
O	M	A	N	I		G	A	S		S	T	I	L	E
R	E	C	A	L	L				S	T	A	B	L	E
A	S	O	C	I	A	L		S	T	A	B	B	E	R
L	I	M	E	A	D	E		K	E	Y	L	E	S	S
	S	A	D	D	E	N		I	N	S	E	R	T	

65

J	A	R	S		T	A	B	L	E	D	H	O	T	E
F	L	E	E		I	R	R	A	D	I	A	T	E	D
O	L	A	V		P	L	A	Z	A	S	U	I	T	E
X	Y	L	E	M		O	S	E		O	L	S	E	N
			N	A	P				C	B	S			
H	O	E		N	E	V		C	O	E		S	A	W
E	N	T	E	N	T	E	C	O	R	D	I	A	L	E
L	E	A	V	E	U	N	F	I	N	I	S	H	E	D
M	A	T	E	R	N	A	L	F	E	E	L	I	N	G
S	T	S		L	I	L		S	A	N		B	E	E
			K	I	A			S	C	I				
S	L	O	A	N		A	W	E		E	N	L	A	I
C	O	R	R	E	C	T	I	V	E		C	A	R	R
O	C	C	A	S	I	O	N	A	L		A	S	I	A
T	H	A	T	S	A	N	O	N	O		S	H	A	Q

66

B	O	O	S	T		A	S	H		M	A	N	I	A
L	U	N	A	R		S	P	I	C	I	N	E	S	S
A	T	O	N	E		O	R	G	A	N	I	S	T	S
C	O	N	T	E		N	E	H	R	U		T	O	N
K	N	E	E				E	F	R	E	M			
M	A	S		H	E	P		L	I	T	E	R	A	L
A	L	T		M	Y	O	P	I	A		W	E	V	E
R	I	O		S	E	A	L	E	G	S		P	A	N
I	M	E	T		S	C	O	R	E	R		A	N	D
A	B	S	I	N	T	H		S	S	S		P	T	S
			C	O	R	E	A				S	E	G	A
A	M	I		R	A	D	I	I		K	O	R	A	N
C	A	N	A	D	I	E	N	S		A	F	I	R	E
T	A	L	K	I	N	G	T	O		L	I	N	D	A
I	S	A	A	C		G	I	N		E	A	G	E	R

67

```
J E S S E J A M E S   R O I L
E X H I L A R A T E   E D N A
O P E N M I N D E D   S I D S
P O L K       S E R I O U S
A R T   V I P S   R E D U C E
R T E   A R E A S   D U S T S
D E R   C O A L E S C E
Y D S   U N C L E A R   A S A
    R U S H I N T O   C U T
S A L E M   Y E T I S   I C H
E M O T E S   D O N S   D C L
D E C I D E D       B R I E
A L A R   R E S T A U R A N T
N I L E   V A N I L L A I C E
S A S S   E L O P E M E N T S
```

68

```
P U B S   A T M   C O L T S
O N A I R   S H A   B L E A T
P A R T I   P E R   S E G N O
E N O   F R I A R S   S A G O
Y I N   T A R R I E R   L E D
E M M A   H E T E R O   S R O
T O U R S     F R A U L E I N
H U N C H   G U S   G E T N O
E S C H E W A L     E A T E N
S C H   B I N D E R   F L O E
A H A   A N G O L A N   E R S
I O U S   O L D A G E   M A T
L I S L E   A G T   S T E N O
O C E A N   N E E   T I N G E
R E N T A   D R S   S T E S
```

69

```
Z U B I N   I L S   P U C E
E R A S E   N O T   H A R T S
A S S E T   S S R   D R A C O
L U T E   S T E A L S   T E C
O L E   P R O N E   A C T I
T A D A   R U N G S   R H E A
    B O Y M E E T S G I R L
E L G A R   E S T   I O T A S
N E U T R O N B O M B S
C A N E   S T A R E   Y U R I
O R G S   S A L E S   R E D
D N A   T O T A L S   P A N E
E I D E R   I N A   J U N T A
S N I D E   O C T   O R I E L
  G N U S   N E E   T E A R S
```

70

```
C A M P S   B I R T H S I G N
O P A R T   O N E R O U S L Y
M O X I E   S A L E S R O O M
B L I M P   S T O N E   L A P
A L M O S T   R A T   L A T H
T O A   I O W A N   S A T E S
    F S T O P   S P I E D
  P A T E N   G L A N D
  P A C E R   S N O R E
P A W E R   C O U P E   U H F
I S N T   Y A P   S T A R E R
E T S   B A S R A   I T S M E
R E H E A R S A L   R O U S E
C L O U D N I N E   E L L I S
E S P R E S S O S   S L A N T
```

71

```
S N O W M A N   G A B F E S T
T E R R A C E   U P R I V E R
R E L A Y E D   N E O N A T E
A D A P T           W E S T S
I I N S I S T   T A N S I E S
T E D   M A I S O U I   V E E
S R O   E N M A S S E   E S S
        J O U S T
E L M   T O T T E R S   I N D
B E E   U S H E R I N   M A E
B A L O N E Y   S A I L I N G
T R I B E           D O T E R
I N S I D E S   E L E V A T E
D E S T I N Y   R O S E T T E
E D A S N E R   E N T R E E S
```

72

```
Q U A S H E S   C A B O O S E
U N S P E N T   O C A R I N A
E Q U A T O R   M A N G L E R
L U N T   S I T E D   A P A R
L O D E   K I T   N I K I
E T E S   S E G O S   S P I N
D E R   R E S H A P E   E N G
        S M A T T E R
S T P   T I B E T A N   S S W
N A R D   S A N E R   R I C A
O P I E   L E N   A T O N
W I N O   T A R T S   C U R T
J O T D O W N   I N D I A N A
O C E A N I C   O E R S T E D
B A R R A G E   N E S T E R S
```

73

```
  C L O S E S H A V E S
  T H E B O S T O N I A N S
V E R Y I N T E R E S T I N G
A N O D E S       T E E P E E
L U N E S   G A D   D R E A M
E R I N   Z E T A S   I R K
S E C   M I S T I T L E S
      C E N T U R I E S
    T O S C A N I N I   P E G
B E N   S L E E K   B I L E
O R A T E   T D S   M I C A S
P A R E N T       D A R N I T
T W O S T R O K E E N G I N E
  L O S E O N E S V O I C E
    M A R T I A L A R T S
```

74

```
  A S T E R I S K   I M A G O
E N T E R I N T O   N O T E D
S T R E E T M A P   B L E N D
T E A   N E O N   A R I S E S
E N D M O S T   F L E E T S
E N D O W   H A I L E R S
M A L E   O B T R U D E
S S E   R O A R E R S   P A H
    C O L L I D E   R E N O
    C A T A L P A   S O R T S
  C A B A L S   M A K E S I T
E R R A T A   W A G E   U L E
R E T R O   E I G H T B A L L
S T E E R   A R E A C O D E S
T E S T Y   R E D S H O E S
```

75

```
R I G M A R O L E   R A M P S
A C R O P O L I S   A A R O N
N O I S E L E S S   T R U L Y
I N T E R L O P E R   E N I D
          N O R   I C E
E W O K   M I S T E D O V E R
S A R A   A L T I   A C E R
T S A R   E L I A S   E R A S
  S N O B   I L L S   A S I T
E A G L E S N E S T   N E D S
T I E   D U O
A L A D   P I C K I N G O F F
L E D U P   S L I D E R U L E
I R E N E   A U T O M A T O N
A S S E T   N E T L O S S E S
```

76

```
F E A S T E R   W B Y E A T S
I N F L A M E   H A V E N O T
A S T O R I A   I N E R T I A
T H E W O R D   T D S   R L S
  E R S T   S T E W   B A S H
J A N U S   A F I N E
A T O P   B U I L D I N G U P
W H O   S A P   A T A   O N E
S E N I O R H I G H   P I S A
    F U R O R   P E T A L
W A D S   I L S A   A L A D
A G O   P C S   M A T I L D A
R E D M E A T   O U T C O L D
E N G A R D E   C L E A N E D
S T E A M E R   O D D N E S S
```

77

```
D O R   C A T C H   A T R I P
A N E   O M A H A   S O U S A
M T A   H U M O R L E S S L Y
E H S   E S E   D E A   S A O
N E O   R E S O L E   I N N
E R N I E S   K I R I   A D E
L O A D   S I N   Z I N C S
L A B E L   O N E   E R R O R
I D L E S   B A R   A O N E
E T E   D R E W   D O N U T S
M O T   O R A T E S   L I P
E R E   I O N   O F T   E N E
L U R I D D E T A I L   T E C
B I M B O   S I D L E   T N T
A N S E L   S A Y E R   E T S
```

78

```
M E R G E   A B O R T   S L A
I V O R Y   M A N E S   H O T
R E S E E   B R E A K S O U T
A R E A S   U N O   T H O S E
G E T T O   S U N   S I T I N
E S T E R   H M O   K N E E D
S T E R E O   A N A   E R R S
      S O N N E T S
S E T A   P E D   E A T S U P
A P A R T   C B S   B R U N O
V I R G O   K A T   B A R K S
A C T O R   L I E   A C R E S
G U A T E M A L A   T H E M E
E R N   R A C E D   H E A P S
D E S   O B E Y S   S A L T S
```

79

```
S E P T A   G A R   P L A T E
U S E R S   E S E   R E G A L
B A T O N   O W S   E A R L S
J U S T A P R E T T Y F A C E
        P E G A S U S
J A G S   P E K O E   Z I T I
U R I A H   D A N S E U S E S
D I A N A   U S O   S N A R L
G E N T L E M A N   T I A R A
E S T A   B A K E R   S C A M
        B R U I S E S
T H E S P O R T O F K I N G S
R A V E L   I T A   A S E A T
A D I E U   E E R   T A S T Y
P A L M S   R N S   E S S E X
```

80

```
  E T H I C S   Q U O I T S
S Q U I S H Y   U R A N I U M
T U R T L E S   I N T E N S E
R I N   E F T   T S E   K A L
I N S E T       S C E N E
F O U L   E S T E E   A R N E
E X P E R T W I T N E S S E S
      M A H A R A J A S
C A M E H O M E T O R O O S T
E V A N   S I S S Y   C B E R
D A R T S       A K E L A
A R I   H A S   A B O   L E I
R I T U A L S   V E R D I C T
S C A R L E T   A T T E S T S
  E L I T E S   S H A N K S
```

81

```
H I T A   M O B I L E H O M E
I S A S   A N A T O M I C A L
G R I P   S T A T I O N E R S
H A L E   S O L O S   T A D A
H E W N         D E N I S
E L I S   C R A S H E D
E I N   R O C K O F A G E S
L T D S   U S H E R   T A X I
S E S A M E S E E D   B C D
    B A T I S T E   C R E E
S C O O P       A I L S
T A U T   A S S A M   L E S T
A N T A R C T I C A   I L I E
T A R G E T A R E A   P L O P
S L E E P I N E S S   H E R S
```

82

```
S T O W   L A S S   A F A T E
H A R I   A C C U S T O M E D
O L A F   S H O E S T R I N G
C O T E   T E N D S   O G E E
K N E A D   D E E   S L O T S
    N I B       M E D
B I R D S O F A F E A T H E R
E L E C T R O N I C P I A N O
N O T H I N G I N C O M M O N
    I L E       A R E
S T A L L   A R C   T S A R S
W E N D   S T E R E   S L U E
I N E R T G A S E S   A I R E
S T R E E T L A M P   K C A R
S H A N E   E W E N   E E L S
```

83

```
P A S S E S O U T   S N I D E
I N T E R P O S E   H E N R Y
M O R A L I Z E R   R E D Y E
P R O N E N E S S   E D I T S
L A B         E E K   T O O
E K E S   C H A R T   W E A R
    O T H E R   H O A R S E
B R O N Z E M E D A L I S T S
L E A G U E   N O N E S
O P T S   S K A T E   T A L K
W A C   M E N         D O E
P I A N O   I N R E S E R V E
I R K E D   F A I R T R I A L
P E E V E   E S P I O N A G E
E D S E L   S T E E P E N E D
```

84

```
T S P   T O S S P O T   J I M
O L E   V O L T A G E   U N A
R E N   S H I R R E D   A S L
N E A R   S P I C E   K N I T
A P N E A   K P H   S N I D E
D O C T R I N E     T O T E S
O N E A C R O S S   I C A R E
    L A S T   T I C K
Q U A I D   S L I N K S O F F
U L N A E   O R A T O R I O
A U N T S   O R C   O U T E R
F L E E   E V E R T   T O R E
F A X   A V A T A R S   L I S
E T E   W A L T Z E S   A L E
D E S   E S S A Y E R   N Y E
```

85

```
I S A D O R A   S O N N E T S
M O B I L E S   W H O O P E E
P R E V A I L   E M P T I E S
E T T E   N O W A Y   A T T A
N O T     P A R     O H M
D U E S   M E N S A   S M E E
S T R O D E   T I R E L E S S
    L O T S   N I T A
V E R A C R U Z   E D I S O N
I C E R   O R E O S   N A P E
O L E     L A O     T E T
L I D S   W I L D E   D I R T
E P I C U R E   L A T E R A L
T S E T S E S   E R E M I T E
S E R V A N T   S P L I C E D
```

86

```
V A N E S S A R E D G R A V E
I T A L I A N A M E R I C A N
N I N E T E E N P E R C E N T
O T O E       E D T   O D E R
      O N L Y Y O U
S P L I N E       B L E A C H
L E A D S T O T H E A L T A R
E T T E     N A E   G O T O
D R E S S T O T H E N I N E S
S O R T I E       L O N E R S
        P L A U D I T
R E M I     C L I   E L I A
E L E C T I O N A D D R E S S
E S S E N T I A L O R G A N S
L E A R N O N E S L E S S O N
```

273

87

```
I B E A M ■ H E L I X ■ P A N
M A D M A G A Z I N E ■ I N E
A L T E R A T I O N S ■ N C O
■ S Y P H O N S ■ R E I N
G R A S P ■ ■ A O N E ■
E O S ■ O B S O L E S C E N T
T S E ■ P U L S A R S ■ E T E
S E A ■ P R A I R I E ■ D R U
U S S ■ I N T E G E R ■ L O T
P A Y I N T E R E S T ■ E M O
■ R A D S ■ ■ I B S E N
H E S A ■ C A S S A V A ■
A R P ■ F L I P O N E S L I D
L E I ■ M A D E B E L I E V E
O D E ■ S P A D E ■ Y E A S T
```

88

```
S O L A R P A N E L ■ B A A S
I N I T I A T I V E ■ A S S T
T E L E P H O N E N U M B E R
I W I N ■ R D S ■ E X O
N A E ■ I F A T ■ S E W S U P
S Y S ■ H E N R I ■ R I T A S
■ R A N K I N G ■ P O L
■ M I D D L E N A M E S ■
S O P ■ S E S A M E S ■
H A V E N ■ T O T E S ■ A B C
A R E N A S ■ N E S S ■ N R A
R A M ■ S A M ■ O N O R
E L E C T R I C C U R R E N T
M E N S ■ A C C U M U L A T E
S E T A ■ H A I R S T Y L E S
```

89

```
P U C K S ■ S P A C E S H I P
A S Y O U ■ L U B R I C A N T
R E C A P ■ U R B A N I T E S
T U L L E ■ R E O P E N ■
S P E A R S ■ E T S ■ T I M E
■ M I Z ■ ■ P I N O N
I N Q U O T E S ■ N E L L I E
S O U N D E D T H E A L A R M
S L A T E S ■ E A T S A W A Y
E A S E L ■ N T H ■
I N I T ■ L A P ■ Y O W L E D
■ H O O R A H ■ O H A R E
J E T E N G I N E ■ T A K E N
E X O R C I S T S ■ E L E C T
D E N S E N E S S ■ R E S T S
```

90

```
T A K E O F F O N E S C O A T
A M A N C A L L E D H O R S E
F I R S T A I D S T A T I O N
T E M ■ N I T ■ E N D
■ S A T ■ A T E S T ■ O N E S
■ O N S ■ H I N T ■
B E D P O S T ■ A R R E A R S
U T O P I A S ■ M O I S T E R
T O O L S U P ■ P A S T E L S
■ R E E L ■ T H E ■
L A P S ■ T W I T S ■ P A T
O V A ■ I M A ■ M R E
T O N S I L L E C T O M I E S
S W E L L E D T H E R A N K S
A S L O O S E A S A G O O S E
```

91

92

93

94

BE MY HEALTHY VALENTINE

L	E	O	N	█	A	B	S	█	V	I	G	I	L	S
E	D	N	O	R	T	O	N	█	I	D	I	D	I	T
I	G	A	V	E	M	Y	L	A	D	Y	L	O	V	E
G	I	N	█	N	E	D	█	G	E	L	█	L	E	W
H	E	D	G	E	█	█	C	I	O	█	L	I	S	A
█	S	O	M	E	B	R	A	N	█	R	A	Z	O	R
█	T	N	T	█	L	E	T	█	I	N	D	E	N	T
█	█	█	█	M	U	F	F	I	N	S	█	█	█	█
I	C	E	A	G	E	█	O	T	C	█	I	F	S	█
C	H	A	R	M	█	S	O	S	H	E	C	A	N	█
H	O	S	E	█	S	I	D	█	B	I	T	E	R	█
A	L	T	█	O	W	N	█	B	Y	E	█	C	E	O
B	E	M	Y	R	E	G	U	L	A	R	G	I	R	L
O	R	A	T	E	D	█	S	U	M	T	O	T	A	L
D	A	N	D	L	E	█	A	R	S	█	B	Y	T	E

95

SHAKE IT ALL ABOUT

I	S	A	A	C	█	S	N	A	G	█	P	H	I	L
M	A	R	I	O	█	H	A	L	O	█	L	O	W	E
P	L	A	N	B	█	A	R	C	H	█	A	S	I	A
█	█	█	T	U	R	N	Y	O	U	R	S	E	L	F
P	O	T	█	R	O	E	█	A	N	I	M	A	L	S
A	R	O	U	N	D	█	█	█	G	P	A	█	█	█
R	I	N	G	█	█	N	E	H	R	U	█	S	H	H
D	O	T	H	E	H	O	K	E	Y	P	O	K	E	Y
O	N	O	█	D	U	D	E	S	█	█	F	I	N	E
█	█	█	A	I	L	█	█	█	B	U	T	T	I	N
F	L	A	T	C	A	R	█	I	R	S	█	S	E	A
R	I	G	H	T	H	A	N	D	O	U	T	█	█	█
A	B	L	E	█	O	D	I	E	█	R	O	A	C	H
I	R	O	N	█	O	I	L	S	█	P	R	O	A	M
L	A	W	S	█	P	O	E	T	█	S	I	L	T	S

96

SHOW TUNES

L	E	W	█	P	E	A	L	E	█	I	T	H	A	D
A	S	H	█	E	R	R	O	L	█	S	U	E	M	E
M	A	I	█	O	N	E	A	L	█	M	E	L	B	A
B	I	G	S	P	E	N	D	E	R	█	L	O	N	█
█	█	I	L	S	A	█	█	A	N	N	O	Y	S	█
P	O	S	S	E	█	S	L	U	I	C	E	D	█	█
S	H	U	█	█	█	O	K	L	A	H	O	M	A	█
S	I	M	B	A	█	B	E	E	█	R	I	L	E	S
T	O	M	O	R	R	O	W	█	█	█	L	T	S	█
█	█	E	N	C	O	D	E	S	█	D	A	Y	A	N
R	A	R	E	S	T	█	█	C	E	O	S	█	█	█
O	T	T	█	█	O	L	M	A	N	R	I	V	E	R
A	B	I	D	E	█	E	A	R	L	E	█	A	R	I
D	A	M	E	S	█	A	T	E	A	M	█	M	I	T
S	T	E	E	P	█	R	A	D	I	I	█	P	E	Z

97

THREE IN ONE

W	E	A	N	S	█	B	L	O	W	█	3	M	E	N
E	L	S	I	E	█	L	U	T	E	█	R	A	V	E
3	M	I	L	E	L	I	M	I	T	█	I	S	A	W
█	█	█	P	U	M	P	S	█	A	N	O	D	E	█
P	A	R	3	█	S	P	Y	█	S	I	G	N	E	R
A	D	O	L	P	H	█	█	M	A	R	C	█	█	█
Y	A	S	I	R	█	S	H	E	E	P	I	S	H	█
S	M	I	T	E	█	T	E	E	█	O	R	L	O	N
█	S	E	T	P	O	I	N	T	█	S	C	O	P	E
█	█	L	A	H	R	█	█	S	T	U	P	O	R	█
W	A	D	E	R	S	█	L	I	P	█	S	E	N	D
E	L	O	P	E	█	S	A	B	E	R	█	█	█	█
L	O	N	I	█	3	P	I	E	C	E	S	U	I	T
C	H	U	G	█	R	O	N	A	█	N	E	R	V	E
H	A	T	S	█	S	T	E	M	█	T	A	N	Y	A

98

PRETTY CUTE

U	M	P	S		A	L	E	R	T		I	W	A	S
P	O	L	E		N	E	V	E	R		R	A	T	A
S	O	U	N	D	N	O	I	S	E		K	I	L	N
E	R	R	O	R		S	L	U	M	P		T	A	J
T	I	A	R	A	S		M	O	E		S	R	O	
S	N	L		B	O	T	H	E	R	S	B	U	G	S
	G	S	A		D	O	I			T	E	P	E	E
		B	R	A	W	N	I	E	S	T				
S	H	U	L	A		D	N	A		A	T	V		
T	Y	P	E	V	A	R	I	E	T	Y		O	A	R
E	G	G		E	R	E		S	A	M	P	L	E	
A	I	R		L	I	D	D	Y		R	O	S	E	S
M	E	A	T		G	R	O	U	N	D	D	I	R	T
E	N	D	S		H	E	L	L	O		E	D	I	E
R	E	E	K		T	W	E	E	D		S	E	E	D

99

COAT OF MANY COLORS

A	S	I	A		I	R	A	N		A	S	W	E	
R	A	M	P		G	E	N	A		B	E	E	S	
A	I	M	S		L	A	G	S		S	T	E	T	
B	L	U	E	C	O	L	L	A	R		A	K	A	
I	O	N		H	O	M	E		A	S	S	E	T	
C	R	E	D	O			F	E	L	I	N	E		
		O	R	A	T	O	R		A	D	D	S		
	G	R	E	E	N	S	L	E	E	V	E	S		
S	U	E	S		N	E	E	D	L	E				
T	I	D	I	E	S			I	D	A	H	O		
A	L	O	N	E		I	A	G	O		P	E	N	
B	T	U		R	E	D	B	U	T	T	O	N	S	
B	I	B	S		R	O	D	S		E	L	S	E	
E	E	L	S		G	L	U	T		S	L	O	T	
D	R	E	W		O	S	L	O		S	O	N	S	

100

C+

P	A	J	A	M	A	S		W	I	R	E	T	A	P
E	L	E	M	E	N	T		I	R	O	N	O	R	E
A	T	T	O	R	N	E	Y	S	A	T	C	L	A	W
L	O	S	S		A	L	E	C		I	L	L	S	
			B	L	E	W		L	P	N				
E	V	A	D	E	S		M	A	R	O	O	N	S	
L	O	U	I	S		C	A	I	R	O		M	I	A
D	I	D	N	T	W	O	R	K	A	C	L	I	C	K
E	L	I		M	A	R	I	E		T	I	T	H	E
	R	A	T	R	A	C	E		C	O	P	S	E	S
			E	N	O		O	M	A	R				
S	P	E	C		I	T	E	M		E	L	A	N	
L	A	Y	I	T	O	N	T	H	E	C	L	I	N	E
I	C	E	P	A	C	K		T	O	O	L	A	T	E
D	E	S	E	R	T	S		A	N	G	E	R	E	D

101

EXPLETIVE DELETED

T	H	E	P	I	T	S		A	F	R	I	C	A	
W	I	R	E	T	A	P		B	R	U	T	U	S	
I	D	O	N	T	G	I	V	E	A	D	A	R	N	
T	E	S	T		U	R	A	L		E	L	I	E	
			O	P	A	L		D	R	Y	E	R		
D	I	D	I	N		L	I	M	O					
A	D	O	R	E	D		S	E	R	B	I	A	N	
H	E	C	K	N	O	W	E	W	O	N	T	G	O	
L	A	S	S	O	E	R		S	T	A	L	E	R	
			T	R	I	P		H	I	L	D	A		
S	T	E	L	E		T	R	A	Y					
A	R	I	A		S	H	A	G		E	L	L	A	
D	O	G	G	O	N	E	Y	A	N	K	E	E	S	
A	T	H	E	N	A		E	P	E	E	I	S	T	
T	S	T	R	A	P		D	E	A	D	S	E	A	

277

102

DOES MY HMO COVER THIS?

E	A	R	F	L	A	P		R	I	B	B	E	D
G	L	O	R	Y	B	E		L	E	C	A	R	R	E
G	E	T	Y	O	U	R		A	C	E	T	O	N	E
	I	N	T	U	I	T	E	D		K	I	D
	V	A	N	S		S	E	N		B	E	E	S
B	O	R	G		T	W	O		T	W	I	N
E	L	M		S	H	A	M	S		E	T	H	E	L
S	G	T		N	O	S	E	O	U	T		E	S	E
S	A	W	T	O		A	T	L	A	S		A	T	A
	I	O	W	A		R	O	W		M	R	E	D
H	O	S	E		L	E	I		D	A	T	E
O	C	T		S	I	N	C	L	A	I	R
W	H	I	S	K	E	D		O	F	J	O	I	N	T
T	E	N	P	I	N	S		B	R	O	O	K	E	D
O	R	G	A	N	S		S	O	N	N	E	T	S

103

VERBAL AGREEMENT

W	A	S	P		W	E	B	S		A	R	T	S
R	A	T	A		A	R	O	M	A		C	O	A	T
I	M	A	W	L	F	O	R	I	T		T	U	B	A
T	I	M	E	I		S	I	R	T	A	I	N	L	Y
E	L	I	D	E	D		S	K	I	D		D	O	I
I	N	N		L	A	B		C	A	V	E	I	N
N	E	A		O	L	O	R	D		A	D	D
			E	W	E	S	A	I	D	I	T
B	A	T		S	T	E	I	N		M	A	D
H	U	M	A	N	E		T	O	G		A	P	R
Y	O	N		C	R	O	C		N	E	E	D	L	E
E	Y	E	C	O	N	C	U	R		S	T	E	E	D
N	A	S	A		S	H	O	E	R	T	H	I	N	G
A	N	T	S		T	E	M	P	O		A	R	T	E
S	T	Y	E		R	O	S	E		N	A	Y	S

104

BACK-TO-BACK VICTORIES

D	E	I	S	M		R	E	A	R		T	E	S	T
A	W	A	K	E		O	L	L	A		E	L	L	A
D	E	N	I	M		D	I	V	V	I	E	S	U	P
		V	O	T	E		A	I	R	T	I	M	E
	A	D	V	I	S	O	R		K	E	E	P	S
S	Q	U	I	R	E		E	L	D	E	R
O	A	T	E	S		I	V	I	E	D		B	L	T
A	B	C	S		S	A	V	V	Y		F	L	O	E
R	A	H		B	O	G	I	E		S	L	A	V	E
	C	A	N	O	N		S	P	I	K	E	S
M	E	S	A	S		G	R	I	E	V	E	D
I	R	A	N	I	A	N		O	L	A	V
T	V	V	I	E	W	E	R	S		K	E	T	C	H
Z	I	O	N		E	R	I	E		T	R	I	P	E
I	N	R	E		D	O	G	S		O	S	C	A	R

105

MIXED CHOCOLATES

A	B	E	L		D	I	S	K	S		A	C	E	D
B	E	L	A		U	N	T	I	E		S	H	A	D
C	A	S	H	T	O	C	O	L	E		T	O	R	A
S	T	A	R	R		O	N	T	H	E	S	L	Y
			A	P	E	D		H	E	R	E
A	C	C	E	N	T	S		R	E	X		A	M	T
L	O	O	T	C	A	C	H	E	S		E	C	R	U
C	R	A	T	E		R	I	P		S	C	O	L	D
O	N	C	E		S	O	C	A	T	C	H	L	E	O
A	S	H		W	O	W		S	H	O	O	T	E	R
	E	T	A	L		I	T	O	R
W	A	S	H	R	A	G	S		C	L	O	S	E
A	L	L	Y		C	O	O	L	C	H	E	A	T	S
R	O	O	M		E	R	N	I	E		W	H	I	P
P	E	T	E		S	E	E	T	O		D	U	R	N

278

106
DIGITAL DICTIONARY

M	A	S	O	N		R	A	C	E		L	I	M	P
A	L	C	O	A		A	R	A	L		E	M	I	R
F	L	O	P	P	Y	D	I	S	K		A	P	S	E
I	S	R		A	M	I		T	E	R	S	E	S	T
O	T	I	S		A	S	T	I		E	E	R	I	E
S	A	N	T	A		H	A	R	D	D	R	I	V	E
O	R	G	A	N	S		P	O	O	H		L	E	N
			B	A	T	S		N	O	E	S			
I	C	Y		P	O	L	O		R	A	C	K	E	T
M	O	U	S	E	P	A	D	S		D	O	N	N	E
M	A	L	T	S		P	E	C	S		T	O	R	N
E	X	E	R	T	E	D		R	U	T		C	O	S
N	I	L	E		T	A	P	E	B	A	C	K	U	P
S	N	O	W		A	S	H	E		L	I	E	T	O
E	G	G	S		T	H	I	N		C	A	R	E	T

107
NOT NECESSARILY WINTER

R	E	B	A		I	B	E	A	M		C	A	N	S
E	R	A	S		N	E	E	D	Y		A	L	O	T
D	A	V	I	D	F	R	O	S	T		R	I	T	A
C	S	A		O	A	R		H	A	N	G	A	R	
O	U	R		S	M	I	T	E		B	E	N	O	T
A	R	I	A		Y	E	A	G	E	R		E	N	E
T	E	A	R	S		S	N	O	W	U	N	D	E	R
			C	O	O				E	P	A			
O	N	T	H	I	N	I	C	E		T	I	M	I	D
N	I	A		L	O	V	I	N	G		L	A	N	E
A	C	U	T	E		S	A	M	O	A		G	O	T
D	E	N	A	D	A		A	P	R		E	R	E	
A	T	T	S		S	L	U	S	H	F	U	N	D	S
T	R	E	T		P	O	S	S	E		S	T	E	T
E	Y	R	E		S	A	N	E	R		E	A	R	S

108
FAUX DIAMOND

T	E	A	S		C	A	R	A	T		R	U	M	S
A	R	T	E		A	B	I	D	E		E	T	A	T
B	A	T	T	E	R	S	B	O	X		V	A	L	E
	S	H	O	A	L			B	A	S	E	H	I	T
	E	U	R		O	P	E	N	E	R				
	A	P	T		W	A	R		S	A	S	S	E	D
E	L	L		V	I	S	O	R		M	E	T	R	O
L	O	A		I	T	E	M	I	Z	E		R	I	M
I	N	T	R	O		S	I	T	I	N		I	C	E
A	G	E	O	L	D		S	E	P		A	K	A	
			L	E	A	S	E	S		C	U	E		
F	O	U	L	T	I	P			M	A	T	Z	O	
A	B	C	S		S	A	F	E	A	T	H	O	M	E
N	O	L	O		E	R	R	O	R		O	N	E	S
S	E	A	N		S	K	I	N	S		R	E	N	T

109
BUYING OPTIONS

S	U	S	H	I		S	C	I	F	I		P	A	Y	S
O	N	E	A	T		C	U	R	L	S		A	S	E	A
C	L	A	S	S		A	R	I	E	L		S	T	A	Y
C	A	S	H	M	E	R	E	S	W	E	A	T	E	R	
E	C	O		E	N	C			S	P	O	R	E	S	
R	E	N	D		R	E	A	C	H		P	R	O	N	E
			U	R	I		R	O	U	G	E		I	D	E
	C	H	E	C	K	E	R	B	O	A	R	D			
R	B	I		N	O	O	N	E		T	R	E			
N	U	T	S	O		P	A	R	D	O		V	E	I	L
S	T	Y	M	I	E			E	F	T		R	N	A	
	C	H	A	R	G	E	D	A	F	F	A	I	R	E	S
C	H	A	R		G	L	I	D	E		K	N	A	V	E
P	E	L	T		O	L	S	E	N		E	S	T	E	R
U	R	L	S		N	A	K	E	D		R	O	A	R	S

110

THE LOVE CONNECTION

L	C	D		P	A	R	E	R		I	S	A	A	C
O	A	R		O	S	A	K	A		N	O	R	M	A
A	P	E		L	I	V	I	D		A	D	M	A	N
F	R	A	N	K	S	I	N	A	T	R	A			
S	A	M	O	A			G	R	O	U	P	I	E	
		O	D	E	S			A	T	O	D	D	S	
R	Y	A	N	O	N	E	A	L			P	A	G	E
H	A	L		T	S	E	L	I	O	T		H	E	W
E	R	I	N		D	I	A	N	A	R	O	S	S	
A	D	V	I	S	E		R	A	K	E				
	S	E	A	T	T	L	E		E	A	G	L	E	
		G	A	V	I	N	M	A	C	L	E	O	D	
S	T	R	A	P		V	O	I	L	A		T	O	G
P	E	A	R	L		E	L	M	E	R		U	S	A
A	L	G	A	E		R	A	I	S	E		P	E	R

111

SERIES WINNERS

G	R	O	P	E		K	E	P	T		M	A	P	S
I	N	N	E	R		I	D	E	A		O	L	L	A
L	A	C	T	O		T	I	C	K		O	K	A	Y
	R	E	D	L	E	T	T	E	R	D	A	Y	S	
S	T	E	R	E	O		I	N	E		L	E	S	
W	A	D	S		C	H	I	N		C	A	I	R	O
A	L	I		K	A	H	N		A	U	G			
M	E	T	W	I	T	H	A	P	P	R	O	V	A	L
			E	S	E		W	O	O	S		A	L	A
S	A	L	T	S		B	E	L	L		S	L	A	V
U	F	O		M	E	L			L	O	U	I	S	A
	B	R	A	V	E	N	E	W	W	O	R	L	D	
W	A	V	E		L	E	A	H		A	T	A	R	I
A	M	E	N		A	P	S	O		L	A	T	E	R
Y	E	S	I		I	S	P	S		S	N	E	A	K

112

TEE SETS

I	R	A	S		E	T	H	I	C		A	L	A	N
C	A	P	P		R	H	I	N	O		L	O	D	E
O	R	E	O		M	E	D	E	A		M	A	Z	E
N	E	X	T	T	I	M	E		T	W	O	F	E	R
			T	O	N	E		E	T	A	S			
P	O	P	E	Y	E		D	A	R	T	T	E	A	M
I	P	A	S	S		B	E	R	E	T		A	G	O
L	E	N	T		B	E	R	N	E		Q	T	I	P
A	R	T		S	O	R	E	S		G	U	I	L	E
F	A	S	T	T	A	L	K		C	O	I	N	E	D
			B	Y	T	E		C	R	A	T			
J	U	L	I	E	T		F	L	A	T	T	I	R	E
A	R	A	L		R	I	L	E	D		H	O	A	X
K	A	R	L		I	D	E	A	L		A	N	N	E
E	L	K	S		P	A	D	R	E		T	A	G	S

113

AROUND THE BANK

S	A	N	D	L		A	Q	U	A		S	A	S	S
S	I	N	A	I		B	U	C	K		E	L	L	A
A	R	E	N	A		D	E	L	I		A	L	I	T
			L	I	N	U	S	A	N	D	L	U	C	Y
S	P	A		S	A	L	T		R	U	D	E	R	
H	E	R	Z	O	G		W	E	E	P	E	R	S	
H	A	L	E	N		O	T	I	S					
	S	O	N	S	A	N	D	L	O	V	E	R	S	
				P	E	S	T		A	C	H	E	S	
L	A	N	D	E	R	S		S	M	O	O	C	H	
A	Z	U	R	E		C	I	A	O		S	T	Y	
B	A	G	E	L	S	A	N	D	L	O	X			
O	L	G	A		T	R	O	I		S	E	A	R	S
R	E	E	D		O	N	T	O		E	N	L	A	I
S	A	T	S		P	O	E	M		D	O	L	E	S

114

HAPPY FATHER'S DAY

```
A I M   E R A   M E T A L S
B R E A D E D   G I V E S U P
B A G H D A D   A M E R I C A
A S S A I L   T R I N I D A D
    B E T R A Y       E S E
S P A     Y I N   P T A
L A V I N   S K E D A D D L E
E P I T O M E   S Q U A R E D
D A D B U R N I T   T Y I N G
    E N S   O E D     P A Y
S I P     I N S E T S
C R A W D A D S   P H O B I A
U K R A I N E   D O O D A D S
B E C K O N S   I S R A E L I
A D H E R E   P E N   R E F
```

115

THAT'S ALL SHE WROTE

```
S L I P   L A S T S   I T S A
P A S O   A D O B E   S E A L
O V E R T H E L O N G H A L L
T E E   O R L A N D O   S A G
T R Y O N   E R E   S C H M O
E N O U G H       S H O O I N
D E U T   A S S A D   A P S E
    S A I N T P A L L
A T A   B L U E S K Y   I F I
M O N T H   G T O   I N N E R
A S T R O S     S N I P E S
    C H A R L E S D E G A L L
P A I D   A L L E N   C A F E
E L L E   S H O E S   I C O N
W E L D   H I T M E   N E R D
```

116

INFER THE ANSWERS

```
C O P I E R S   A N T E A T E R
O N A N D O N   G O I N G A P E
D O W N S O U T H   I N D I X I E
A R N I E   B R A S   N I C K
    E L F   U S E U P
A R T S   O M I T   N E T P A Y
L I E   I R A S   A S P E R S E
T A X I D E R M Y S T U D I O S
A T A L O S S   I H O P   E N E
R A N K L E   S E E P   I D E S
    S E G A L   S O D
E T A L   A L D A   P L A C E
C H R I S T M A S T R E E L O T
C O O L H E A D   R U N S F O R
E R N I E E L S   A T S T A K E
```

117

THE YEAR 2000

```
C H A D   S T O P   A S P I E
O U Z O   L A D E   I W I L L
D R U M M A J O R   R I C E S
S T R E A M   R O O M M A T E
    D I M E   T H E M
A C E   T E L L   I N A S E C
C U P   A R C A R O   S C A R
R O S S I   A L E   S K A T E
I M O K   C R A G G Y   N I P
D O M I N I   W A R S   T N T
    M A N S   L A T E
T H O M M C A N   M E L O T T
E E R I E   F I L M M A K E R
S M E L L   E L I E   N I N E
S I L K Y   S E E R   D E S K
```

281

118

AN I FOR AN EYE

Y	I	N		T	W	O		S	T	E	P	S	O	N
E	R	O	S	I	O	N		H	E	R	O	I	N	E
L	A	S	A	G	N	A		A	R	O	U	S	E	D
P	S	Y	C	H	O	L	O	G	I	S	T			
			T	U	L	L				S	A	D	E	
R	A	W	E	S	T		E	M	M	A		M	U	D
A	T	O	M		M	O	O	D	S	W	I	N	G	
C	O	N	I	F	E	R		A	S	K	A	N	C	E
I	N	T	R	O	V	E	R	T		S	O	A	R	
N	C	O		B	A	D	E		Y	E	A	R	N	S
G	E	N	A			D	I	E	S					
		S	U	B	C	O	N	S	C	I	O	U	S	
U	P	A	T	R	E	E		A	M	O	N	G	S	T
R	E	P	O	S	E	D		P	A	R	S	L	E	Y
N	A	R	R	A	T	E		T	N	T		E	R	E

119

NOBLESSE OBESE

B	R	E	W	S		M	O	M	S		S	C	R	A	M
R	A	V	E	N		A	L	A	N		C	U	O	M	O
R	E	A	L	E	S	T	A	T	E		O	P	C	I	T
		F	A	T	T	Y	A	R	B	U	C	K	L	E	
T	I	R	A	D	E			D	A	T	A	S	E	T	
U	S	E	R		R	E	N	T		N	I	K			
B	E	B	E		E	N	U	R	E		N	E	S	T	S
B	E	E		P	O	R	K	Y	P	I	G		N	A	M
Y	A	L	T	A		Y	E	M	E	N		M	A	X	I
		H	R	S		D	E	E	T		O	F	I	T	
S	T	R	E	A	K	S			A	M	B	U	S	H	
C	H	U	B	B	Y	C	H	E	C	K	E	R			
R	E	N	A	L		H	A	L	L	E	L	U	J	A	H
A	D	O	B	E		M	I	K	E		B	L	A	D	E
P	A	N	E	S		O	R	E	O		A	E	S	O	P

120

THE WEDDING SINGERS

I	N	F	O		T	E	L	E		T	A	N	G	Y
D	E	A	F		O	X	E	N		A	K	I	R	A
T	H	I	N		F	I	A	T		L	A	G	E	R
A	R	L	O	G	U	T	H	R	I	E		H	A	D
G	U	S	T	O			A	S	S	E	T	S		
		E	L	V	I	S	P	R	E	S	L	E	Y	
M	A	G		F	O	C	H				T	I	G	E
A	T	O		S	W	E	A	T	I	T		F	U	N
M	O	O	G			W	A	R	E		E	N	S	
A	N	D	Y	W	I	L	L	I	A	M	S			
	E	L	N	I	N	O			P	O	S	S	E	
E	T	O		P	A	U	L	S	T	O	O	K	E	Y
A	I	S	L	E		N	E	H	I		T	O	A	D
S	M	E	A	R		G	A	I	N		H	A	R	I
T	E	R	M	S		E	D	N	A		E	L	S	E

121

EXPLODING FIREWORKS

D	R	A	G		W	I	S	E	S	T		C	U	D
O	H	N	O		A	N	T	O	N	Y		A	P	R
M	O	D	E	R	N	C	A	N	A	L		R	A	E
		S	E	D	A	N		F	E	I	N	T	S	
J	A	C	O	B			B	U	R	S	A	R	S	
A	L	A	N		M	A	R	I	S		A	L	E	E
W	I	N		G	O	M	E	R		N	A	D	E	R
	N	O	R	M	A	L	D	A	N	C	E			
A	D	E	L	E		Z	A	I	R	E		M	E	N
B	U	D	D		S	E	X	E	S		F	O	R	E
R	E	M	E	L	T	S			A	R	N	A	Z	
A	D	O	R	E	R		C	I	S	C	O			
D	A	R		R	O	M	A	N	C	E	L	A	N	D
E	T	A		O	V	E	R	D	O		I	G	O	R
D	E	L		Y	E	L	L	O	W		C	O	D	Y

122
SOUNDS OF THE PAST

L	A	C	K		S	T	R	A	P		A	C	D	C
E	T	R	E		K	O	A	L	A		D	O	E	R
F	L	I	P	S	I	G	H	E	D		M	A	C	E
T	A	T	T	L	E			S	K	I	L	L	S	
I	N	T		A	D	O	R	E		A	T	B	A	T
S	T	E	A	M		L	E	V	A	R		I	R	E
M	A	R	T		N	E	V	E	R	M	I	N	E	D
		O	E	D			I	A	N					
J	A	Z	Z	B	A	N	N	E	D		C	A	R	S
A	V	E		S	K	E	I	N		C	A	M	E	O
M	E	A	D	E		O	P	E	R	A		P	T	A
A	R	L	E	N	E			A	S	T	E	R	N	
I	R	A	N		C	I	T	Y	W	A	R	R	E	D
C	E	N	T		H	O	V	E	L		Y	E	A	S
A	D	D	S		O	U	S	T	S		A	S	T	O

123
EXPRESS YOURSELF WITH CLOTHING

W	O	K	E		S	T	R	A	P		B	E	S	S
I	R	I	S		N	I	E	C	E		E	T	T	U
L	I	S	A		A	D	D	L	E		T	H	A	I
L	O	S	I	N	G	Y	O	U	R	S	H	I	R	T
E	L	M		O	S	U			K	Y	O	T	O	
D	E	E	P	S		P	O	E	S	Y		P	O	R
		O	E	D		H	M	O		P	I	U	S	
	P	A	S	S	I	N	G	T	H	E	H	A	T	
B	E	V	Y		N	E	O		O	N	E			
R	T	E		E	G	A	D	S		D	W	E	L	L
A	P	R	I	L			C	P	U		L	E	I	
W	E	A	R	I	N	G	T	H	E	P	A	N	T	S
L	E	G	O		E	N	O	L	A		L	I	S	T
E	V	E	N		W	A	G	E	R		I	N	G	E
R	E	D	S		S	W	A	P	S		T	O	O	N

124
FORE! CRYING OUT LOUD

Y	I	P	S		A	M	M	O		S	W	O	R	D
E	A	R	P		B	E	A	R		H	E	N	I	E
S	C	O	R	E	C	A	R	D		A	P	A	C	E
M	O	P	E	D			S	A	N	D	T	R	A	P
A	C	H	E	S	O	N		I	C	E		O	R	E
A	C	E	S		P	I	A	N	O		O	L	D	S
M	A	T		H	A	L	L		A	L	L	O	T	
		H	O	L	E	I	N	O	N	E				
G	A	M	U	T		B	U	R	T		C	P	R	
A	M	I	D		P	R	I	M	E		S	O	R	E
S	I	D		L	O	A		B	O	L	E	R	O	S
C	A	D	D	Y	I	N	G		P	E	N	C	E	
A	B	L	E	R		G	R	E	E	N	S	F	E	E
P	L	E	B	E		E	A	R	N		T	E	E	D
S	E	C	T	S		D	Y	E	D		O	D	D	S

125
LETTER OPENERS

B	A	R	B		F	L	U	T	E		M	A	R	E
O	R	E	O		R	A	Z	O	R		A	R	E	A
X	R	A	Y	V	I	S	I	O	N		Y	S	E	R
K	I	D	D	E	D			S	C	H	E	L	L	
I	V	E		R	A	C	E	R		H	E	N	I	E
T	A	R	R	Y		B	V	I	T	A	M	I	N	S
E	L	S	A		B	R	A	C	E	S		C	G	S
		T	A	R	A		H	A	M	S				
H	E	B		B	A	D	G	E	R		A	B	C	S
I	C	L	A	U	D	I	U	S		O	N	E	U	P
T	O	U	R	S		O	N	T	A	P		T	R	A
S	C	E	N	E	S			R	U	S	H	E	R	
H	I	R	E		T	B	O	N	E	S	T	E	A	K
O	D	E	S		A	R	L	E	N		E	R	L	E
W	E	D	S		G	R	A	T	A		W	E	L	D

126

BUM STEERS

```
N A A C P ■ T A S S ■ E A R L
O C C U R ■ I N C A ■ A R E A
T E R R A ■ T E R M ■ R A G S
■ H O L Y C O W A B U N G A S
H I S S E R ■ ■ M A N H O L E
A G T ■ R E N D ■ D A N E S
W H I P ■ C A R O L E R ■ ■
■ ■ C A S H C O W A R D S
■ ■ S H E L V E D ■ T I D Y
A B A S E ■ E D I E ■ D E E
D O U B L E S ■ ■ E X C E P T
M R S O L E A R Y S C O W L ■
I N T O ■ L U C E ■ I V I E S
R E E K ■ E T A T ■ S E T T O
E O N S ■ D E S I ■ E T H E L
```

127

VOICE VOTE

```
A S S A I L S ■ D I S P O S E
C H A R I O T ■ O N P A P E R
H U R R I C A N E C E N T E R
E T A ■ ■ K R I S ■ W I S P S
■ ■ T W E R P ■ R E C ■ ■
U P S H O T ■ I C E D ■ A L S
S I T A R ■ N U N ■ C R A M
E Q U I N E U T T E R A N C E
R U M S ■ M P H ■ ■ A R I E L
S E P ■ N I C E ■ V I L E S T
■ ■ S A T ■ B W A N A ■ ■
A S C A P ■ S U E S ■ ■ P I A
S T O M A C H D I S T R E S S
P A R O L E E ■ R A V I O L I
S T E A M E D ■ D R A G N E T
```

128

MY ACCESS CODE GOT PINCHED

```
H A L T ■ S I T S ■ T O P S [PIN]
A G E E ■ O D I E ■ E T H A N
T R A N S A L [PIN] E ■ N O I S E
[PIN] E S ■ U K E ■ R E S O L E D
S E T A S I D E ■ L I L I ■ ■
■ ■ C A N ■ R I F L E P I T
A C O R N ■ B A S I E ■ [PIN] T S
S U [PIN] E ■ M A S O N ■ R E B A
T R I ■ K A R E N ■ L O S E R
A B O V E P A R ■ D E N ■ ■
■ N A I L ■ S T R E A K E R
[PIN] N A C L E S ■ R E C ■ N R A
T O T A L ■ [PIN] C U S H I O N S
O N E T O ■ A P E S ■ S L I [PIN]
S E D E R ■ L A D Y ■ A L E G
```

129

YOU ARE WHAT YOU EAT

```
A B E S ■ P U T ■ C O S T A R
L E T L O O S E ■ O T O O L E
P E T E R P A N ■ R I P P L E
S T U D M U F F I N S ■ B O D
■ ■ S E P ■ O K S ■ R A Y S
A L S ■ ■ H U E ■ P E N ■
L A W M A K E R ■ M O H A I R
T I E C L I P ■ A T L A N T A
O R E G O N ■ G I V E B A C K
■ T E E ■ Y A M ■ ■ S H E
E R I E ■ L O U ■ S I S ■
L E E ■ C O U C H P O T A T O
M A P P E D ■ H E A T E D U P
O R I O L E ■ O R N A M E N T
S M E L L S ■ S O S ■ S E E S
```

130

A CHANGE OF CLOTHING

M	E	T	S		H	U	N	T		S	A	T	I	N
A	Q	U	A		O	B	E	Y		A	L	O	N	E
L	U	N	A		S	O	C	K	I	T	T	O	M	E
T	I	E	B	R	E	A	K	E	R		A	L	A	
E	N	D		F	A	T	S		E	R	R	A	T	A
S	O	U	N	D				E	S	T	E	S		
E	X	P	O		S	I	R	I	C	A		E	S	P
			W	H	I	T	E	C	A	P	S			
A	R	C		I	N	E	V	E	R		P	S	S	T
H	I	R	E	D				R	A	C	E	R		
S	P	A	D	E	S		M	O	P	E		A	G	E
	T	W	A		C	O	A	T	O	F	A	R	M	S
F	I	L	M	S	H	O	R	T	S		L	E	E	S
A	D	I	E	U		P	I	E	S		D	U	N	E
D	E	N	S	E		S	O	R	E		O	P	T	S

131

ABOUT MY HMO ...

S	T	E	W		U	B	O	A	T		T	S	A	R
T	E	A	R		T	A	N	D	Y		A	H	M	E
U	R	G	E		A	L	T	O	S		L	O	C	O
F	R	E	N	C	H	M	O	R	O	C	C	O		
F	A	R	C	E			P	E	N	A		T	A	J
			H	O	S	T			S	A	D	I	E	
B	R	R		S	P	A	N	I	S	H	M	O	S	S
Y	E	A	S		A	C	U	T	E		A	W	L	S
E	A	R	T	H	M	O	T	H	E	R		N	E	E
A	D	I	E	U			E	K	E	D				
R	E	N		G	I	S	T		A	O	R	T	A	
	T	R	E	N	C	H	M	O	R	T	A	R	S	
H	O	O	T		L	O	U	I	S		E	T	A	S
M	A	G	E		A	N	G	E	L		L	I	M	E
O	T	O	S		Y	E	S	N	O		L	O	S	T

132

FISCALLY PHYSICAL

M	A	I	D		H	A	W	K		S	P	E	E	D
U	G	L	Y		A	S	H	E		O	H	A	R	A
T	A	L	L		P	A	Y	T	H	R	O	U	G	H
A	T	B	A	T			S	T	E	R	N			
T	H	E	N	O	S	E		L	A	Y	E	G	G	S
E	A	T		B	L	A	M	E	D		C	A	N	E
			B	O	I	S	E		V	A	L	U	E	
	F	O	O	T	T	H	E	B	I	L	L			
A	F	L	A	T		T	R	O	L	L				
P	A	A	R		E	L	A	I	N	E		A	M	I
B	A	N	D	A	G	E		C	O	S	T	S	A	N
			G	R	A	V	E		T	O	W	I	T	
A	R	M	A	N	D	A	L	E	G		M	E	T	O
M	I	A	M	I		N	I	L	E		E	L	A	N
A	G	R	E	E		T	A	K	E		I	L	I	E

133

THE CALL OF THE DODO

S	I	B	S		G	R	A	B		D	E	A	L	T
T	R	A	P		R	O	R	Y		A	N	N	O	Y
R	O	N	A		I	S	C	R	E	W	E	D	U	P
A	N	A	T	O	M	Y		O	W	N		I	V	E
P	I	N	U	P			S	T	E		P	R	E	S
S	C	A	L	E	N	O	T	E		S	T	O	R	E
			A	R	E	N	A		P	L	A	N	E	T
B	A	A		A	S	A	R	U	L	E		S	D	S
O	N	S	E	T	S		D	R	U	I	D			
A	T	O	N	E		L	O	N	G	G	R	E	E	N
S	I	N	O		I	A	M		H	E	N	R	Y	
T	H	E		E	S	P		M	U	S	I	C	A	L
F	E	M	A	L	E	D	E	E	R		S	O	S	O
U	R	A	L	S		O	T	I	S		E	D	E	N
L	O	N	G	A		G	E	N	A		R	E	D	S

134

BARRELS OF FUN

```
M A G I   A Q U A   N A I V E
A C E D   R U S T   O I L E D
S H E L L F I S H   C R I E S
H E N I E   P R O M O T E R
  D A N T E     M A U I
    G U N T H E E N G I N E
A P T   P O R E     T H R E W
B O A R   S A N T O   T A M E
C O C O A     C A N A   S O S
S H O O T T H E B U L L
    F L E E     S L I M E
  B O T A N I S T   O Z O N E
C A R O N   F I R E W A T E R
C R E P T   E D E N   R O M A
S A L S A   R E E D   D R Y S
```

135

CAN THEY CUT IT?

```
C A M P   A F I R E   W A S P
O V E R   L A D E N   E L L A
P O L I T I C A L Y E S M A N
I C A N S E E   A A A   A V A
L A N C E   C A Y   T U N I C
O D I E   R A I S E   S A S H
T O E   P U R R   A M E C H E
    C A B D R I V E R
S P R U C E   A G E D   P O D
M O O R   S P I N S   C O P E
O T T E R   A D O   V A S E S
O S H   A P R   R E C L I N E
T H I R D R A T E W R I T E R
H O R A   E D D I E   C E N T
S T A G   P E S T S   O D D S
```

136

PERSONALITY DISORDER

```
D O N   R E E D   S C A L E D
I N A S E N S E   A L G O R E
V E S P U C C I   G O E A S Y
I N T O P A R S L E Y
D O I T   S O M E   E A S E L
E T E   M E W   R E D N O S E
S E R I F   P O L   G A P E
    P L A I N O Y S T E R
P E L E   D O T   B L I G H
A S O F N O W   O H S   N R A
L E Y T E   A N N E   S E E R
    R O Y A L I S T P E N
D E J A V U   D I S K E T T E
I N A S E C   E N T I T L E S
P E R I S H   R E S T   Y D S
```

137

NET NOMENCLATURE

```
W P A   S C A R C E   S H I N
O I D   H A R B O R   G E N E
E G O S U R F I N G   T A R T
I S R A E L     F O P   R U T
S K I M   M B A   O S S I E
M I N   G R A Y B A R L A N D
E N G   L E N A   S T A Y S
    R I C E   A S I T
  G O U D A   A L E C   H M O
M O U S E P O T A T O   O O P
I N T E R   F A N   M U L E
R E C   S S N   C O R D O N
A M O K   C O B W E B S I T E
G A L A   O T O O L E   N O R
E D D Y   W E A K L Y   I V S
```

138

POSTSEASON GAMES PEOPLE PLAY

```
R I F T ■ S P A ■ C A B O T ■
E R L E ■ P A L ■ E L I T E S
S O U P B O W L ■ R A T T L E
U N S E A T ■ I B E ■ S O L D
M O T E L ■ Z E T A S ■ M I A
E R E ■ I F I ■ U L L M A N N
■ E R A ■ I N N ■ B E I N G S
■ ■ P U N C H B O W L ■ ■
E R R I N G ■ L E W ■ E T C
R E E N T E R ■ E L M ■ H A M
A P T ■ O R B I T ■ A N I T A
S O A P ■ B I O ■ A T O N A L
E S K I M O ■ W A S H B O W L
S E E S A W ■ A L I ■ L U B E
■ S N A R L ■ N E T ■ E T A T
```

139

NOW PLAYING AT THE MEGAPLEX

```
L O F A T ■ T R O N ■ E P P S
A B A S H ■ W A C O ■ T R I S
D O T H E R I G H T T H I N G
L E A ■ G E N E S ■ R I V E T
E S L ■ A P E D ■ B O C A ■
■ A M M O ■ A M I S T A D
B E T T E ■ S H O W S ■ E N O
E A T S ■ S H U N S ■ I B E T
E R R ■ S L I D E ■ L O E W E
P L A T O O N ■ B O N N ■
■ C O L T ■ P O O R ■ J E B
O U T D O ■ B O U N D ■ A P O
A L I A S J E S S E J A M E S
K N O T ■ A B E T ■ I V I E S
S A N E ■ R E D S ■ M E N S A
```

140

GENDER-NEUTRAL POETS

```
S R I ■ A P R ■ P B S ■ D E B
L E C A R R E ■ O U T S I D E
O N A N D O N ■ P R O U D E R
B E N J O N O F F S P R I N G
■ ■ O R E ■ A L T ■ ■ ■
I G L U ■ A N Y ■ D O F F S
R H O ■ B A I L ■ P A N O U T
W A L T E R D E L A H O R S E
I N L O V E ■ T O L L ■ T E N
N A S T Y ■ B T U ■ P E S O
■ ■ H U E ■ A G O ■ ■ ■
J O H N B E R R Y P E R S O N
O N A R O L L ■ E S T E L L A
A T L A R G E ■ W E A S E L S
N O T ■ G A Y ■ S S T ■ D A H
```

141

THEY DO AND I DO

```
J U K E ■ P I L A F ■ M O O S
U N I S ■ I C O M E ■ A C T I
T I E T H E K N O T ■ J E T T
■ O L E A R Y ■ R A S ■ L A I
I N B E D ■ W A L K D O W N
S I A M ■ D A H L ■ I O T A S
A S S ■ M U S E ■ A R I ■
■ T A K E T H E P L U N G E
■ A M Y ■ L E O N ■ O A F
A S T R O ■ S I Z E ■ G O G O
T H E A I S L E ■ L A D L E
L E X ■ R U E ■ C L A U S E
A R M S ■ G E T H I T C H E D
S P E C ■ A V A I L ■ H O Y A
T A X I ■ R E P A Y ■ O W E D
```

142

THE REEL THING

```
MESO FREON ACTS
AVOW LEARN DRAT
CAMERACREW HYPE
GSA EGAD ROSIE
RILED PROJECTOR
AVID UPUP ACE
WEANS AMINO LAD
  ACID NERD
TBS ADORE TASTE
IRE REBA LEAN
MOVIESETS MIAMI
EMEND RIDE SAG
LIRA GRATEDFILM
ANEW PECAN IDEA
GERE AVERY NESS
```

143

3 45s

```
WAD LEWIS ALIT
ARID IWONT RATA
REVOLVERCALIBER
STENO FOREARM
AHS UGH MTV AID
WATT LOSES ADZE
  ALIBI FLOES
JUKEBOXRECORD
VANES TEACH
HITS OHYES ACRE
FLU ABE FTD REL
BREWERS ITALL
FINALYEAROFWWII
ORES ETHEL OLEO
EDDY DOLCE SST
```

144

ONLINE CONNECTIONS

```
ADE PABST FORTS
MOM ELATE ADORE
AMI GASOLINETAX
ZINE IREAD HIT
ONETRACK MORITA
NONCOM CAMERON
SST TIBIA DART
  BONETIRED
HIVE TANYA FTD
AMIABLE ASPIRE
SANDRA PINETREE
AGT ALLAN LEAP
FINETOOTHED MDS
INERT STOLE ALE
TERRY SITIN NET
```